P9-CEB-295

APR 19 1995

ERRATUM

Through an error, the copy on the jacket states Professor
Virtanen is a graduate of the University of Michigan. He received his B. A. with honors at the University of Wisconsin in
1932. Subsequently, he also received his M. A. and Ph. D at
the University of Wisconsin.

CLAUDE BERNARD

CLAUDE BERNARD
1813-1878

AND HIS PLACE IN THE
HISTORY OF IDEAS

Reino Virtanen

UNIVERSITY OF NEBRASKA PRESS
LINCOLN: 1960

Publishers on the Plains

UNP

TO MY DAUGHTERS,
ALICE AND VIVIAN

ACKNOWLEDGMENTS

I wish to express my thanks and appreciation to my wife, Sylvia B. Virtanen, and to my colleague, Professor Boyd G. Carter, for reading this study in manuscript and suggesting improvements; to the staff of the University of Nebraska Libraries for many services; to the Administrator of the Collège de France for allowing me to delve in the Claude Bernard Archives; and to the University of Nebraska Research Council which granted me aid in the form of a Faculty Summer Fellowship, as well as travel and typing expenses.

Acknowledgments are due to the following authors and publishers who authorized the quotation of copyrighted material: Henry D. Aiken; Dr. Léon Delhoume; Doubleday and Company; Harcourt, Brace and Company; *The Bulletin of the History of Medicine,* Johns Hopkins Press; Alfred A. Knopf, Incorporated; W. W. Norton and Company, Incorporated; Principia Press; University of Wisconsin Press; Librairie Armand Colin; Harvard University Press; Cambridge University Press; Librairie Alphonse Lemerre; Technology Press; Charles C. Thomas, Publisher.

Contents

Introduction

CLAUDE BERNARD'S career had little of the drama which the public has found in the life of his younger contemporary, Louis Pasteur. His physiological discoveries, if no less important, had few of the striking, even sensational features that made Pasteur the subject of best-selling books and popular films. There is nothing to match the interest and suspense of Pasteur's work on rabies in Bernard's research on the glycogenic function of the liver. The revelation of the body's internal environment was hardly as dramatic as the unveiling of the microscopic world of bacteriology. But Pasteur's sparkling exploits in applied science are counterbalanced by the contributions of Bernard to the principles of investigation, and in their own way his achievements were quite as significant. It does not detract from the stature of Louis Pasteur to affirm that the older man was a scientist of equal rank. Indeed, Bernard deserves some credit for teaching his junior, and this is a debt which Pasteur gladly recognized. Both men were great experimentalists, consummate laboratory technicians, but one dealt mainly with physiological functions and the other concentrated on the microscopic realm. Usually their work was in separate fields, although in a crucial instance—the question of spontaneous generation—their researches came into conflict.

While a considered judgment accords Bernard a comparably high position in the history of science, his is a figure lacking in lustre for the public eye. On the other hand, Pasteur's name is absent from the annals of literature and philosophy, whereas Bernard's most famous book, the *Introduction to the Study of Experimental Medicine,* is associated through Émile Zola with the rise of naturalism in the novel, and is compared by Ernest Renan and Henri Bergson with the *Discourse on Method* of René Descartes. There is, to be sure, one point at which Pasteur touched the current of general ideas, and it is a point that concerns Bernard as well, if only posthumously. When, in 1882, Pasteur was admitted to the French Academy, it devolved upon him to pay his respects to the leading apostle of Auguste Comte, namely Émile Littré, for he was filling the vacancy left by the latter's death. He seized the opportunity to assail the Positivist

1

philosophy on behalf of the "Infinite," and thus established his place as the favorite scientist of the *bien-pensants,* who saw in science a threat to their traditional beliefs. The devoutly Catholic Pasteur made a sharp division between the domains of science and religion, leaving ultimate problems to the jurisdiction of Faith. His attack on what Charles Renouvier called "scientisme" was aimed not only at Comte and Littré but also at Taine and Berthelot. By repercussion it also implicated the late Claude Bernard, generally regarded as the exponent of scientific determinism. In the polemic directed a few years later against "scientisme" by the Brunetières and the Paul Bourgets, Pasteur could be considered a useful ally, come over, as it were, from the enemy camp. Bernard could hardly be accorded this somewhat questionable honor.

If we may pursue this comparison into their private lives, it is apparent that the Fates gave the advantage here to Louis Pasteur. Happily married to a woman who admired and encouraged him in his researches, Pasteur could well have aroused the envy of Claude Bernard. Mme Bernard not only was unsympathetic toward her husband's work but succeeded in having their two daughters share this hostility. In her opinion Bernard would have done better to apply his energies toward a prosperous medical practice instead of tormenting helpless animals in his laboratory. To make amends for his activities, she contributed money to antivivisectionist societies. The sharp misunderstanding which divided Bernard from his family provided the theme for Zola's first project for his novel *Le Docteur Pascal.* The novelist confided to Edmond de Goncourt: "I am tempted to model this scientist upon Claude Bernard. . . . A scientist married to a bigoted woman, who would destroy the results of his labors as he works."[1] The final version of his book, however, has little in common with this plan. Anyone who has read in the private correspondence some of the bitter reproaches addressed to her husband by Mme Bernard may well feel that their unhappy story of incompatibility was best left unpublished.[2] Separating from her, Bernard eventually found quite platonic consolation in a sedate attachment to Mme Raffalovich, a Russian lady living in France who was interested in science and philosophy.

The family life of Pasteur, even the sorrow attendant upon the loss of three of his children, forms an appropriate backdrop for the career of the scientist. In Bernard's case there is a partition between his personal life and his scientific work. In a letter to Pasteur he expressed his sympathy for Pasteur's bereavement, which he could readily understand, having himself suffered the deaths of his own two infant sons.[3] For both men their work was a resource and consolation, but for Bernard it was even more—it was an escape and a refuge. One of his best biographers, J. M. D. Olmsted, is right to end his book with the words Bernard wrote to Mme Raffalovich: "Science absorbs and consumes me; I ask no more if it helps me to forget."[4] The present study, therefore, will concentrate on his intellectual life which was, if not the whole, certainly the larger part.

That life forms an essential chapter in the history, not only of science, but of general philosophical ideas as well. But to speak of the philosophy of Claude Bernard may require some justification, for it is well known how often he disclaimed any metaphysical purpose. Devoting his energies to experimental work and intent on being left free to pursue it, he had no interest in becoming embroiled in philosophical controversy. He kept the door of his laboratory closed against the winds of doctrine, and even his study door was, if not hermetically sealed, at least seldom left open to them.

His research was concerned with such explosive topics as the nature of life and death, and despite his reticence, was likely to arouse suspicion among men of traditional beliefs. Along with Berthelot, he was regarded as one of the high priests of materialistic science. Already, for all his reserve, he had become a symbol of that science that had driven the hamadryad from the wood and was threatening one of the last sanctums of orthodoxy, the seat of life. The Goncourts, for example, saw him in this light. Consider the caricature presented in this witticism from the *Journal*:

It was said that Berthelot had predicted that after a hundred years of physical and chemical science, man would know the nature of the atom, and with this science could at his will regulate, put out, and re-light the sun like a Carcel lamp. Claude Bernard for his part was reported to have announced that after a hundred years of physiological science, one would be able to make laws for organisms and carry out human creation in competition with the Creator Himself.

We made no objection, but we do believe that when science has reached that point, the good Lord with white beard will arrive on earth with his key-chain and tell mankind, just as they do at the Art Show at five o'clock: "Gentlemen, it is closing time!"[5]

The fact that Bernard explicitly denied more than once that it was possible to create life did not prevent this sort of story from circulating. He was already almost a figure of myth. He had enough opponents in his own domain—followers of Cuvier who questioned the value of experimenting on living things, followers of Bichat who stood fast by the doctrine of vitalism, members of the medical profession who scoffed at laboratory work. He did not need to look outside for bones of contention. But for all his concentration on his special task, he could neither stop others from drawing philosophical inferences nor refrain from thinking about philosophy himself.

No less than four of the commentaries devoted to him bear the title of the philosophy or the metaphysics of Claude Bernard. Many of the others deal with philosophical ideas. These interpretations are so variant that it is difficult to find one which would muster the agreement of the majority of students. As for systematic historians of philosophy, they have not always found it necessary to distinguish him from the Positivist school of his age. To list him summarily among the followers of Comte is to obscure his role as an independent intellectual force, functioning not only during his own time but in some areas right down into the twentieth century. It is a striking fact that leaders of recent and contemporary science like Walter B. Cannon, Sir Charles Sherrington, and Norbert Wiener acknowledge the seminal value for their own work of certain contributions of Claude Bernard. The field seems open for one more attempt to define the philosophical bearing and the general influence of his work. It is hoped that the author will be found justified in saying little about technical physiological matters although dealing with one who, as Pasteur and Paul Bert repeated after J. B. Dumas, was not merely a physiologist but was in his time physiology itself.[6]

CHAPTER One

The Career and Writings
of Claude Bernard

CLAUDE BERNARD was born on July 12, 1813, in the wine-growing region of Beaujolais at the village of Saint-Julien near Villefranche-sur-Saône. Wine-growing had been the occupation of the family for generations. Even after settling in Paris, he never broke his link with the country of his childhood. Almost yearly he would repair to his vineyard to recoup his strength after his labors in the laboratory and classroom. From his land one could on clear days catch a view of the Alps far away on the other side of the Saône River.

His father died while Claude was still only a child, but his mother was to live to see her son becoming a famous man. His youth gave little sign of the greatness he would attain: he was not an outstanding pupil. Nor were the courses he studied calculated to prepare a coming scientist: Latin, French, history, a little mathematics, but no science and no philosophy.[1]

5

At 19 he took a job in a pharmacy in Lyon. The backwardness of pharmaceutical practice in those days is suggested by an oft-quoted anecdote of an incident in the apothecary shop. When the young Bernard was on the point of throwing away some drugs he thought could no longer be used, his employer stopped him, saying: "It would serve to make theriacum." And the leavings of miscellaneous drugs were collected in a container reserved for the purpose. After such an episode one might fancy oneself to be in the shop of Fleurant of Molière's *Le Malade imaginaire*. Nevertheless his few months in the almost mediaeval pharmacy undoubtedly helped Bernard to acquire that manual skill in the handling of apparatus which later impressed his teacher Magendie. Studying medicine, however, was far from his thoughts. He had not yet found himself.

After leaving the apothecary, he wrote a light comedy or *vaudeville* of which only the title is known. This playlet, *La Rose du Rhône,* was evidently produced with some local success in Lyon. He was tempted to try his hand at a more ambitious dramatic work. In these early 1830's, the advent of Romanticism was somewhat delayed in the provinces. Thus his historical drama *Arthur de Bretagne* is closer to the spirit of Casimir Delavigne than to that of Victor Hugo or Alexandre Dumas *père.* Although it echoes the current vogue of historical drama, with its imitation of Shakespeare's *King John,* it fails to reflect the color and vividness of *Hernani* or even of *Henri III et sa cour.* Written in conventional prose with its long rhetorical speeches, it lacks the fire of dramatic genius.[2] But Bernard was encouraged to hope for success in the capital. Armed with a letter of introduction to a royal librarian, he made his way to Paris in 1834, and submitted the play to the consideration of Saint-Marc-Girardin, an influential critic of the period. The latter, who was not impressed, persuaded Bernard to abandon the thought of a career connected with the theatre.

Diverted from *belles-lettres* to the study of medicine, Bernard knew the hard life of the impecunious medical student in the Paris of the Bourgeois Monarchy under Louis-Philippe. But unlike the Bianchon of Balzac's *Comédie humaine,* his path led away from the practice of medicine. Before becoming an interne in the Hôtel-Dieu, he had already attended some lectures of the famous Magendie. His dexterity as a dissector caught the notice of the crusty *savant*, who engaged him as his assistant at the Collège de France. Though his future was still not assured, this proved a decisive step for the young Bernard. As the outstanding French experimental physiologist of the day, Magendie gave him the guidance and confidence he needed at a time when the science itself as well as Bernard's own plans were still somewhat amorphous. Thus one might almost say that Bernard and the science of physiology matured together. The influence of the experimentalist Magendie was crucial not only positively but also negatively for Bernard's career. For the state of physiological science, suffering from lack of uncontested data and clouded by metaphysical fancies, required just that kind of factualism of which Magendie was the strongest exponent. Magendie, who was fond of calling himself the *chiffonnier* of physiology, was accustomed to assert that what the science needed was not *mind* so much as *eye* and *hand*. Nothing is so revealing of the attitude of Magendie as the story of one of his demonstration lectures. Having announced to his audience what he expected to prove with his experiment, he reacted with delighted laughter when the demonstration proved just the opposite.[3] He would often initiate an experiment "pour voir"— to see what would happen, without having any notion of the result in advance. It was necessary for the continued progress of the science that someone schooled in the pure experimentalism of Magendie, someone imbued with his reverence for fact, should then react against this raw empiricism and proclaim the value of theory, or rational interpretation. This was to be the capital role of Claude Bernard. He would further the work of his master by denying him, providing the antithesis which would incorporate the thesis of Magendie in a higher synthesis.

In 1843 Bernard won his doctorate with a dissertation on gastric juice, the first fruit of a study which was to lead him into an ever-widening investigation of the process of digestion and body fluids. From a highly specific problem he worked his way to matters of more general bearing. But it is a characteristic of his entire research career that he never lost touch with the particular initial problem. One of his star students who was to desert science for politics, Paul Bert, outlined in his obituary address the principal discoveries of Bernard. This account shows how Bernard's researches moved from the digestive juices and the discovery of the glycogenic function of the liver and the nature of diabetes to the phenomena of animal heat, the function of the blood in regulating body temperature, to the discovery of the two types—dilating and constricting—of vasomotor nerves.[4] In his obituary article, Dr. Chauffard wrote that even if Bernard had not described the laws of animal glycogenesis, he would remain the leader of modern physiology through his discovery of what Chauffard called "la double innervation vaso-motrice."[5] Each of these particular studies led to concepts of broader significance. Thus from an understanding of digestion grew the realization that there exists no absolutely fundamental gap between herbivores and carnivores, or even between the animal and vegetable kingdoms. In this way he laid the foundations for the subject of general physiology. His studies of the vasomotor nerves prepared the way for the concept of the sympathetic nervous system. Almost all Bernard's discoveries go back to his beginnings, a period of some seven years from 1843 to 1851, which has been likened to an explosion of productivity. All of these researches led to the study of the chemical life of the cell.

One of the most fruitful techniques he developed was the use of toxic agents in physiological investigation. The strange effect of a South American poison, curare, which head-hunters daub on the tips of their arrows and spears, had puzzled scientists ever since the poison was first reported by Europeans. The victim, while losing all power to move a single muscle, remains aware of things going on around him until coma and death set in, and is not attacked by the convulsions usually associated with poisoning. Bernard's explanation of the toxic action of curare first brought him to the attention of a broader reading public. In an article in the *Revue des Deux-Mondes,* he described how curare destroys the motor nerves, but leaves intact the sensory nerves, the muscles, and all other tissues, hence the horrible fate of the victim, who retains consciousness while reduced to an inertia without hope. But more significant for the progress of physiology was the way in which Bernard utilized this and other poisons for the exploration of the organism.[6] The method was called a sort of bloodless vivisection. Nowadays biochemists possess in isotopes a more subtle instrument, which need not, like the poisons, injure the subject. But the principle is similar. These agents are like detectives sent to probe the living organism. Their selective sensitivity yields exact but highly specific data. Bernard showed that poisons do not produce a general effect on the organs but a unique change on the anatomic level. Thus carbon dioxide combines with the hemoglobin of the blood and brings about asphyxiation by preventing the absorption of oxygen. Curare, on the other hand, attacks the ends of the motor nerves and by paralyzing respiratory movements, produces asphyxiation in a different manner.

Many are the stories related by students and visitors as well as Bernard himself illustrating the difficulties he had to cope with in carrying on his work: limited funds, rudimentary equipment, unhealthful conditions, danger of infection, interference, misunderstanding. His laboratory was a dank, unwholesome cellar where, according to Renan, he perhaps contracted the illness which was to shorten his life.[7] It required unusual courage, determination, skill, and faith in science for him to persevere. These obstacles were, of course, faced by other French scientists of his time. But there was one difficulty which particularly affected the physiologist: vivisection was not calculated to win the sympathy of tenderhearted members of the public. There is the story of the courteous Quaker who visited the laboratory of Magendie and Bernard in an effort to persuade them to renounce vivisection. There is the more amusing story of the police chief's dog. Bernard often related how, having purchased a dog from one of his suppliers, he applied a silver cannula to its stomach. Later he learned that the animal had escaped to the street. A brush with the law threatened when the dog returned home with the instrument attached to its body. Its master was the police *commissaire* of the *quartier!* Bernard was able to convince the police official that he had bought the dog in all innocence and that the apparatus had not really harmed it— a statement which the animal helped to prove by its lively and playful behavior. The happy outcome was that Bernard could now continue his experiments with the blessing of the authorities.[8] Dangers of another sort hung over him. Once at the Alfort slaughterhouse he was severely bitten on the hand by a horse, apparently afflicted by glanders. It had been maintained by Rayer that this terrible equine disease could also be carried to man. Renan's account of the incident is brief but unforgettable: "Wash it quickly!" said Rayer who was at his side. "No, don't wash it!" cried Magendie. "That will hasten the absorption of the virus!" There was a moment of hesitation. "I'll wash it," said Bernard putting his hand under the faucet. "It's cleaner that way."

Upon the death of the physiologist Pierre Flourens, Bernard succeeded to his chair in the French Academy. That the nature of Bernard's discoveries was still not perfectly understood even by the cultivated lay public is shown by the anecdote reported by the Goncourt brothers in their *Journal:* "Right now, it's really funny, Claude Bernard's reception at the Academy is delayed because Patin is unable to make his speech in reply. The unhappy Patin forgets daily at the bottom of the staircase the physiology the physiologist had just taught him in his study."[9] The same mishap would have been unlikely with the more spectacular discoveries of Pasteur. The election crowned the reputation which Bernard had won with the publication of his *Introduction to the Study of Experimental Medicine* in 1865—a book he might never have written had not ill health compelled him to take a rest from his experimental labors. This enforced leisure, spent largely at his childhood home among the vineyards of Beaujolais, gave him the time and the detachment necessary for the exposition of his scientific philosophy.

Although other official honors came to him, among them membership in the Imperial Senate, these years of his public success were not years of happiness. The Franco-Prussian War was for him, as for his friends Renan and Berthelot, a time of severe trial and distress, of disillusion and grief for his stricken country. During these latter years, which were further saddened by illness and estrangement from his family, he took refuge in his work and in periodic sojourns at Saint-Julien, where he continued to spend the late summer and early fall. He was rewarded by the progress made by his disciples, Dastre and

D'Arsonval, although another student, Paul Bert, tempted by politics, was being lost to science. Among those who attended his lectures at various times were the Americans S. Weir Mitchell and N. P. Bowditch, the Russian Sechenoff, teacher of Pavlov, the Dominican Father Didon. (Most accounts agree that he was a poor lecturer.) His long friendship with Mme Raffalovich was not only a sentimental attachment but also to some extent a collaboration. She helped him by translating foreign writings for him and they often discussed his work together. On New Year's Day in 1878, he caught cold. It turned into nephritis, and he died on February 10 after a painful illness.

Bernard's final living moments were the subject of a controversy which has not even yet been definitively resolved. What was the nature of his religious beliefs at the end of his life? The forms of the procedure prescribed by the Church were undoubtedly observed. What about the content? What were his feelings? Did he harbor some skeptical "pensée de derrière la tête" in his last days? Perhaps some answer to these questions can be hazarded in the concluding chapter.

Such questions were not the subject of the only debate consequent upon his death. The relationship between Bernard and his younger contemporary Pasteur had been one of mutual regard and admiration, occasionally of collaboration. But an event took place a year after Bernard's death which provoked what might be called a posthumous rift. Some unfinished research notes found in Bernard's papers were published by his students and Berthelot. These notes contested the famous views of Pasteur on anaerobic bacteria and the biological nature of ferments. Pasteur was hurt by what seemed Bernard's lack of candor and infuriated by Berthelot's disingenuous procedure. Bernard had hoped to demonstrate that alcohol could be formed without yeast cells, a chemical hypothesis sharply contrary to Pasteur's belief that fermentation could not take place without life. Eighteen years later Eduard Buchner was to obtain a soluble ferment by applying pressure to yeast cells. This later work had the effect of vindicating Bernard and seemed to invalidate Pasteur's position. The latter was right in what he affirmed, wrong in what he denied, to use an expression which Bernard once applied in a different context. The debate between Berthelot and Pasteur was embittered by the intrusion of metaphysical considerations. Pasteur saw in Berthelot's action an effort by the materialist camp to promote the notion of spontaneous generation in the face of his own decisive refutation of any such phenomenon. Bernard had certainly not tried to demonstrate spontaneous generation; but in asserting that fermentation could occur in the absence of live yeast cells he was in effect aiming at a chemical explanation of what Pasteur regarded as a vital phenomenon *sui generis*. Bernard had already commented elsewhere on the predilection of chemists for evoking vitalistic forces—and Pasteur was originally a chemist—although this could not, of course, be said about the chemist Berthelot. What is significant in the Pasteur-Berthelot episode is the way in which a rather technical question could cause repercussions in the sphere of philosophical and religious ideas.[10]

The Writings of Claude Bernard

The past two decades have seen a marked renewal of interest in the writings of Bernard. Several book-length treatments and many shorter studies have appeared, both in France and the New World. This is partly a result of the posthumous publication of some collections of notes and letters which had lain for decades among his private papers or in charge of his pupil D'Arsonval. They are valuable for the interpretation of some of his ideas, and throw a good deal of light on the man himself, on the workings of the mind of a scientist whose demeanor in public was reserved and impersonal. Yet they do not change radically the conception we can derive from the writings published during his lifetime. They illuminate and liven, they do not revolutionize, our conception of Claude Bernard. The works he published remain basic.

The most rewarding for the layman is still the *Introduction to the Study of Experimental Medicine*. To this may be added various articles from the *Revue des Deux-Mondes* collected in *Experimental Science (La Science expérimentale)*, which also contains his address to the French Academy delivered upon his entrance in 1869.[11] His courses of lectures given at the Collège de France and the Museum comprise fourteen volumes published between 1855 and 1879. Of these there were two containing discussions of a general and philosophical nature: *Lectures on Experimental Pathology (Leçons de pathologie expérimentale)* (1871), and *Lectures on Vital Phenomena Common to Animals and Plants (Leçons sur les Phénomènes de la vie communs aux animaux et aux végétaux)* (1878-9).[12] The latter sets forth the latest and the most far-reaching exposition of his biological thought. It is therefore one of the most important of his works. But if these *Leçons* are essential for a full appreciation of his achievement, none of them has the historical importance of the *Introduction to Experimental Medicine.* They were college courses; the *Introduction* was an event.

It won him entry into the French Academy. Émile Zola used it as a foundation for his theory of the "experimental novel," and thus made it one of the capital documents of late nineteenth-century literary history. Such outstanding figures of French thought as Ernest Renan, Ferdinand Brunetière, and Henri Bergson have paid it the highest of tribute. The book has been mentioned repeatedly, in the same breath with Descartes' *Discourse on Method.*[13] It has become a classic of scientific literature. It is used, for example, as a text in the *philosophie* year in French lycées. In fact only Dr. Pierre Mauriac, brother of the novelist, has been paradoxical enough to deny its greatness, feeling perhaps like the Greeks who tired of hearing Aristides called the Just.[14]

The principal reason for its appeal lies in the fact that it goes beyond the scope indicated by the title, beyond the author's expressed aim to apply the principles of the experimental method to medical science. The first part is an essay on the philosophy of the experimental method, and a rationale of scientific discovery. The second part is an exposition of the principle of scientific determinism in its application to biological science. Consequently, both of these sections have a bearing for the philosophy of science which transcends the field of medicine. The third and concluding part brings to the principles enunciated a fascinating array of illustrations from the author's busy laboratory, thus distinguishing him from the general run of philosophers of science who must pick the brains of research scientists for examples of their analyses. For this reason a recent writer has called the book almost unique in the history of science.[15] In the interesting collection of texts on intellectual discovery and artistic creation published by Brewster Ghiselin under the title *The Creative Mind,* there are included reports from theoretical scientists like Poincaré and Einstein. But there is nothing by an experimental scientist. An appropriate selection for such a volume could be made from Bernard's *Introduction.*

What makes the book still so interesting today is the clarity and precision with which the author brings the experimental method home to us in its concreteness. He begins with an analysis of *observation* and *experiment.* Cuvier and before him Zimmermann had described observation as passive and experiment as active: "The observer listens to nature; the experimenter questions nature and forces it to reveal itself."[16] Bernard points out that the separation between the two, apparently so obvious in the abstract, becomes more doubtful in practice. Observation too may be active; that is, it may be intentionally pursued in accordance with a preconceived idea. Experiment no doubt has an intentional aspect, but its distinguishing feature is the comparison of two conditions, or sets of conditions. To prove that mere intervention by the scientist in natural phenomena does not constitute experimentation, Bernard cites the famous case, reported by Dr. Beaumont, of the Canadian woodsman whose stomach had remained exposed as the result of a hunting accident. By mere happenstance, Dr. Beaumont was enabled to study the process of digestion in a living man. A physiologist in a laboratory could not have done more by means of the vivisection of one of the higher animals. But neither instance is an experiment, for neither involves comparison with another set of conditions. On the other hand, the comparative aspect of experimentation comes into play even when, as in Pascal's barometric investigations, no change is imposed on the course of natural phenomena. Pascal's researches consisted of the comparison of barometric conditions at different atmospheric levels.

Even a science of observation like astronomy can derive benefits from the comparison of observational data. But the fundamental distinction between observation and experiment remains. An experiment is an induced observation, "une observation provoquée." Experimentation involves a disturbance imposed on nature. The effect of this disturbance must be compared with the natural state. "The observer must be the photographer of nature. . . . He must observe without preconceived ideas. . . . He listens to nature and writes under her dictation."[17] Bernard calls himself the "secretary of nature" as Balzac had called himself the "secretary of society."[18] On the other hand, the experimenter interrogates nature, but must hold his peace when she answers. Unlike the observer, he has his preconceived idea which he submits to nature, but he must be ready to change or abandon it depending on the response he receives. Paul Bert recalls that when he entered Bernard's laboratory as an assistant, and was divesting himself of his overcoat, the master told him: "Leave your imagination with your overcoat in the cloakroom, but pick it up again when you go out."[19] In experimental science the difference between observer and experimenter is largely theoretical. In practice the two advance side by side, are indeed the same person.

In the second chapter of Part One, Bernard describes the role played by the mind in experimental research. His analysis is not the schematic sort we expect from a logician of scientific method, his approach is that of an active laboratory man, yet he rightly feels that he is making a contribution to scientific methodology. A noteworthy formulation is that of the interrelations between thought and reality, of the dialectical play between theory and experimental fact. "The experimenter poses his idea like a question, an interpretation anticipating nature with more or less probability, from which he logically deduces consequences which at every moment he confronts with reality by means of experiment." He designates this idea by the term *sentiment* which should not be understood in its English connotation. The steps in the process are outlined as follows:

> In the quest for truth . . . the *sentiment* always has the initiative, it engenders the *a priori* idea or intuition; reason then develops the idea and deduces its logical consequences. But if the sentiment must be clarified by the light of reason, reason in turn must be guided by experiment.[20]

Sentiment here refers to the hunch or flash of insight which comes to the scientist faced with a problem to be solved. It may be aroused by a chance observation in the course of an experiment, or as a corollary of a theory being tested, but it always has its point of origin in nature, in observed reality: "Experimental ideas are not innate. They do not arise spontaneously; they require an occasion or an external stimulus."[21]

Experimental method is not sufficient by itself to produce discoveries. Research is an art, and not everyone has the flair for catching the meaning of experimental data: "Method alone produces nothing, and it is an error of certain philosophers to have ascribed too much power to method in this regard."[22] Discoveries are not produced mechanically, but require the participation of the mind. Yet it would be wrong to assume that Bernard regards the mind as primary. The mind does not create scientific facts from its own substance, but derives them from experience of the external world.

As science advances, the body of knowledge gains greater precision and coherence, but in any growing science some part will remain provisional and approximate. A growing science, in fact, is one in which we find a continual process of review, of check and countercheck. That is why methodic doubt, a constant questioning of one's assumptions, must be a basic principle of science. It is the methodological doubt of Descartes. The work of the experimental scientists involves a perpetual interaction between reason and nature, between thought and external reality. It is not a question of induction as against deduction. Bernard argues that the separation between induction and deduction is an artificial one which cannot be maintained in practice. His remarks point in the direction of the modern view of the matter summarized by André Lalande: "This contrast is only partial: we pass from one to the other by the simple development of our knowledge; chains of deductive ideas become incorporated more and more into the conduct of experiment and 'experimental reasoning.' "[23] It is Bacon's emphasis on induction at the expense of deduction which explains his failure to make any significant discoveries in science. Descartes' methodological doubt is more fruitful than Bacon's tables of inductive procedure.

Developments which have taken place in the philosophy of science since Bernard doubtless have reduced the value of his exposition. Some of what he wrote belongs to his own time and has lost vital interest for us along with the productions of Taine, Comte, and Spencer. But certain ideas of Bernard take on a new interest when viewed from our present standpoint. We are struck by his conception of scientific theories as intellectual instruments which serve us for penetrating into the web of phenomena. The roots of the pragmatism or instrumentalism of Peirce, James, and Dewey are of course in the period when Bernard worked and wrote. Although he was himself no pragmatist, his formulation is a suggestive one, and not far removed from Dewey's instrumentalism, not to mention Bridgman's operationalism:

> In science the great precept is to modify and change one's ideas as science advances. Our ideas are but instruments which help us to penetrate into phenomena. We must change them when they have fulfilled their function, as we change a dull lancet when it has served long enough.[24]

Later in the same chapter he contrasts the scholastic philosopher with the experimentalist in much the same way as Dewey will distinguish the contemplative from the scientific mode of inquiry:

> It is precisely the Scholastic who thinks he possesses certainty who gets nowhere. . . . And it is, on the contrary, the experimenter who continually doubts and who does not think he has absolute certainty about anything, who succeeds in mastering the phenomena around him and extending his power over nature. *L'homme peut donc plus qu'il ne sait.* Man can do more than he knows. Genuine science gives him power only while showing him that he is ignorant.[25]

The full import of this turn of thought can be made evident only by reference to other works of Bernard. It is one of those seminal ideas which have preserved Bernard's *Introduction* from the relative obsolescence that has been the fate of contemporary books like Herbert Spencer's *First Principles* or Hippolyte Taine's *De l'Intelligence.*

There are no limits to the principle of experimental doubt except the determinism of phenomena. The scientist is sustained by faith in the possibility of unraveling this determinism from the intricate web of events: "The *absolute determinism* of phenomena of which we are conscious *a priori* is the only criterion that directs and sustains us."[26] Although more difficult to establish because of the greater complexity and variability of vital processes, determinism is as true for the science of life as for the inanimate world. This is the topic of the Second Part of the *Introduction*. The discussion falls naturally into two divisions. The first chapter deals with "experimental considerations common to living things and inanimate bodies"; the second sets forth "experimental considerations special to living things." The critique of vitalism with which Bernard opens the first chapter has lost some of the sting which it had in his day. That is, of course, an indication of the success of this very critique. To appreciate its pertinence for his first readers it is only necessary to recall how Taine in 1862 described the usual acceptance by physiologists of the notion of vital force: "Physiologists usually conclude in accepting a *vital force*. Some conceive it as an invisible fluid; others, as an immaterial being; still others, as something inexplicable and beyond the reach of the human mind."[27] More familiar with current trends than Taine, Bernard recognized that the older vitalism was on the way out, but its influence still survived to encumber the path of scientific investigation. The question even came up in the Senate in 1868. On this famous occasion, Sainte-Beuve, evoking the respected name of Claude Bernard, valiantly defended the freedom of scientific education against those who would have curtailed the teaching of antivitalistic views regarded as materialistic and irreligious.[28] For vitalists life was a mystery which experiment might destroy but never explain. Against this obscurantism Bernard asserted the validity of experimentation in biology. The properties of living things, he affirmed, are linked to physicochemical phenomena which regulate their appearance.[29]

The experimental method does not aim at answers to transcendental or metaphysical questions on the "riddle" of life. Physiology is a science that looks only for the material conditions in which vital phenomena manifest themselves. It seeks only the proximate cause. Scientific determinism means simply one thing and no more: The conditions of a phenomenon once known and fulfilled, the phenomenon must occur. That is as true for biology as for physics. Knowing these conditions, the scientist becomes the master of the phenomenon, being able to reproduce it at will. He need not know the "why"—knowing "how" suffices. Bernard is eloquent on the potentialities of science: "By a wonderful compensation, as science humbles our pride, it increases our power."[30] This activist note is sounded again and again by Bernard. It is one of the marks of the modernity of his thought.

A more special instance of his modernity is the concept of the internal environment. If living things seem to be relatively independent of external conditions, it is because they possess their own internal environment. The *milieu vital* is what distinguishes the organic from the inorganic world. The second chapter of Part Two outlines the consequences which this entails for experimental procedure. The physiologist is compelled to recognize an organic harmony in living things which is lacking in the inanimate realm. This interrelationship of the parts of an organism had led Cuvier to deny that experimentation could be applied to living beings. But while acknowledging this interdependence, Bernard insists that organic processes can nevertheless be isolated from each other sufficiently to allow experimental analysis. Digestion, circulation, and other processes can be separated from the organic whole and studied in themselves. On the other hand, Bernard is aware of the danger of stopping there. To lose sight of the harmonic unity of the organism is to take away its intrinsic character. Therefore physiological analysis must be followed by physiological synthesis. Bernard is as conscious as any vitalist that what characterizes the organism is not the physicochemical properties of its elements but the unity of its processes. Like Comte, Bernard warns against any mechanistic tendency to reduce biology to physics and chemistry.

Bernard's insistence on the inherent difference between organic and inorganic has not always been understood. Some of his concessions to the vitalists are more verbal than substantial. They have been distorted by readers who are in fundamental disagreement with his whole purpose. Such are his formulations of the "directive or creative idea," the *quid proprium* of life. A later chapter will be devoted to a closer analysis of this problem of interpretation. Here it may be sufficient to emphasize that whatever the apparent implications of certain phrases, his argument is this: Life can and must be studied experimentally. Furthermore, while admitting that life is more than physics and chemistry, the physiologist must concentrate on the physicochemical conditions, in both the external and internal environments, in which vital phenomena are manifested. Physiology is a distinct science with its own methods and its own criteria, but it must utilize physics and chemistry as auxiliaries.[31]

Anatomy itself is only an auxiliary to physiology. The study of structure is only the beginning. Vital functions must be studied in the living organisms. One of the principal methods must therefore be vivisection. The pages in which Bernard discusses vivisection are memorable for their simple reasonableness. The sentimental arguments advanced by antivivisectionists are cogently refuted. The cause of human health is adequate justification. Why should men, who exploit animals for food, for clothing, for sport and transport, refuse to other men the right to employ animals for experiment when the aim is to cure and prevent human suffering? Claude Bernard, who was confronted in his domestic life with misunderstanding on this score, might have been pardoned some impatience with his adversaries. Yet his discussion is free from harshness or recrimination. As for human vivisection, his remarks seem quite sensible. The right to experiment on humans cannot be denied as a matter of principle. If experiments can be devised which could cause no possible harm, they are permissible if the results seem worth while. Yet the moral responsibility involved is certainly a heavy one, and Bernard does not say the last word on the ethical aspects.[32]

Living creatures are almost incredibly complex, and the higher one mounts on the scale of life the greater becomes the diversity. It is no wonder that some scientists have quailed before these difficulties. One of the trail blazers in that heroic age of physiology, Bernard was cutting a path through an almost impenetrable jungle. An indispensable tool was the now familiar method of comparative experiment. Of two animals as similar as possible, one is made the subject while the other is retained as the control. The two animals are placed in the same conditions, minus one; and it is the effect of this condition, present for one animal, absent for the other, which the experimenter tries to compare. But the procedure requires the utmost skill and perfection of technique, the sharpest alertness and sensitivity on the part of the investigator. One reason is that no two animals are ever exactly alike, no one animal is always the same from one moment to the next.[33]

This individual variability makes the application of mathematics to physiology somewhat premature. The significant concrete fact may be lost when an average is established. Averages are legitimate only when the facts are comparable, simple, and measurable. Bernard cites one absurd example: "Le sublime du genre a été imaginé par un physiologiste qui, ayant pris de l'urine dans un urinoir de la gare d'un chemin de fer où passaient des gens de toutes les nations, crut pouvoir donner ainsi l'analyse de l'urine moyenne européenne!"[34] Because of the imperfect state of science, Bernard questions the value of statistics in medicine. His opposition to statistics has been held against him. But a contemporary philosopher of science has recently defended him: "Claude Bernard, probably the most striking opponent of statistics in biology, never dreamt of objecting to statistics as investigative aids. Rather, he disapproved of the replacement of data by numerals or formulae. Mach and Einstein made the same point relative to physical events."[35] Bernard's skepticism was justified in the field of medicine because the physician has to treat individual patients, not statistical fictions. Every effort must be made to pass beyond the stage of merely statistical probability:

> Statistics, in my opinion, is of use only in directing the observer toward the research for this undetermined cause, but it can never lead to any real law. . . . By basing itself on statistics, medicine could never be more than a conjectural science; it is only by basing itself on experimental determinism that it will become a true science. . . .[36]

With this characteristic emphasis on scientific determinism we end the outline of the Second Part of the *Introduction*.

The Third Part is entitled "Application of the Experimental Method to the Study of the Phenomena of Life." These pages have a unique value in the literature of science. By means of concrete examples drawn from his research and that of his associates, Bernard clarifies the principles enunciated in the theoretical sections. The reader gains a vivid appreciation of the practical problems of laboratory procedure. This is more than a mere recital of experiments; it is a critical analysis of experimental operations. Bernard warns against being satisfied with negative or contradictory observations. Scientific criticism should bear on facts and not on words. We are often dupes of such terms as life, death, disease. Science must lay aside unknown forces. Physiologists must aim in the direction of reducing vital properties to physicochemical properties, and not vice versa. Finally, and this may serve as a conclusion to the *Introduction* as a whole, experimental medicine must reject philosophical systems while keeping alive the philosophical spirit, for it is the philosophical spirit that animates the quest for knowledge by unceasingly stirring up unsolved problems.[37]

Casting a glance backward over the book, one has to acknowledge that it is not free from faults of composition and expression. In parts repetitious, sometimes verbally inconsistent, occasionally digressive, the work is not perhaps a model of formal perfection. It is, however, basically consistent throughout, an example of clear, cogent exposition, full of meat and substance. A characteristic that must have become evident is the author's gift for trenchant statement, for striking maxims that, once read, are not soon forgotten. "L'homme peut plus qu'il ne sait." A capital event in the scientific annals of its time, this is a book which has not exhausted its value for our own day.

Of the other writings published by Bernard, the articles he contributed to the *Revue des Deux-Mondes* are of interest because, like his *Discours Académique,* they were addressed to a lay public. Collected in book form soon after his death, under the title *La Science expérimentale,* they include such important pieces as "Problèmes de la physiologie générale" (1867), "Des

Fonctions du cerveau" (1872), and "Définition de la vie" (1875). It is worth citing one example. The essay on the functions of the brain forcefully advances a concept that Bernard had already broached in his Academy Discourse.[38] This idea is nothing less than the validity of physiological study of the brain as the organ of thought. He boldly brushes aside the obscurantist opinion that the mechanism of thought must forever remain a closed book to us. We must renounce the view that the brain constitutes an exception in the organism, that it is merely the "substratum" of a mysterious activity that is outside the purview of physiology. Aside from the greater complexity of the phenomena involved, the brain is as much an organ as are the heart and the larynx. With this article, Bernard stakes out a place as one of the forerunners of modern scientific investigation of the brain.[39]

Of the posthumous publications, the most attractive for the general reader are *Le Cahier rouge* and *Lettres beaujolaises*. *Le Cahier rouge* was published by Dr. Léon Delhoume in 1942. Much has been made by some recent commentators of this collection of miscellaneous notes which Bernard left in a little red notebook. Does not Dr. Mauriac seize upon it as providing proof of his reconstruction of an anguished Claude Bernard?[40] This would be a misleading description of a booklet which contains some interesting thoughts and reflections but which hardly constitutes a sensational document. A number of these fragments are valuable for tracing Bernard's ideas in the decade before the *Introduction* was published. But the occasional expression of interest in religion cannot be taken to prove any deeper religious feeling than could be surmised from reading the *Introduction*. There is no warrant for using these notes to demonstrate an evolution of Bernard toward religious faith. A more complete discussion of this whole matter must be deferred until the concluding chapter, but it is significant that no decisive evidence of a Bernard *pascalisant* can be found in the volume of correspondence published under the title *Lettres beaujolaises*.

These letters, brought out by Justin Godart in 1950, are selected from Bernard's correspondence with Mme Raffalovich. Bernard was a man of extreme reserve in his personal contacts. His unhappy married life had something to do with the air of reticence which he turned to the world. This makes the letters he wrote to Mme Raffalovich indispensable for a study of his personal life. But even here his inner personality remains partly veiled from our view. His relationship to this Russian lady resident in Paris was a sedate and entirely proper one which scarcely transcends the plane of a warm, largely intellectual friendship. There is nothing comparable with the relationship between John Stuart Mill and Mrs. Taylor, much less with that of Anatole France and Mme du Caillavet. Even the more personal parts of the letters express no passionate feeling. The writer does unbend now and then, but it is usually to throw off some humorous sally. Bernard was fond of puns. There was, for example, at Saint-Julien the bench he called his "banc de Sisyphe." On one typical occasion when Mme Raffalovich had been reading the psychologist Alexander Bain, he wrote to her: "Puisque vous êtes dans le Bain, je vous demanderais ce que ce philosophe bienfaisant pense de la volonté: Je médite quelque chose sur la physiologie de la volonté."[41] * Some of the letters picture the scientist on his visits to Saint-Julien and express his ardent love of nature. The letters dating from the time of the Franco-Prussian War give vent to the grieved reactions of the writer to his country's misfortunes. Still others, like the one just cited, deal with a variety of scientific and philosophical questions, and exhibit Mme Raffalovich as a collaborator reporting to the scientist on her reading of English and German works in the field.

Noteworthy among the posthumous publications is the uncompleted *Principes de médecine expérimentale* whose discovery we owe to the scholarly detective work of Dr. Delhoume. One of the clues which started Dr. Delhoume off on his search for the missing treatise was the following statement in the *Introduction:* "The two volumes which will make up my treatise on the *Principles of Experimental Medicine* will be exclusively devoted to the elaboration of procedures of experimental investigation ap-

---

*"Since you are in the Bain [*bain* means *bath*] I'd like to ask you what that beneficent philosopher thinks of the Will. I am considering working up something on the physiology of the Will."

The play on the name Sisyphus refers to six yew trees behind the bench ("six ifs"—Sisyphe).

In another connection, he told Berthelot of an infallible method for freeing oneself gracefully from the long-winded monologues of Chevreul when one paid a visit to the venerable chemist: "Interrupt him with a pun. He will stop to think it over. You then seize the opportunity to take your leave respectfully."

plied to physiology, pathology, and therapeutics."[42] The edition now in our hands corresponds imperfectly to this prospectus. Inevitably it lacks the unity and organization of a finished product, and indeed it has some of the features of an *omnium gatherum*. The editor did as well as anyone could with materials the author had not cast into coherent shape. Many a passage reads like a palimpsest of the *Introduction*. One example is the comparison made of Descartes and Bacon to the disadvantage of the latter.[43] Another instance of repetition is a page inspired by Pascal's fragment on the theme that man prefers the hunt to the prize.[44] Portions of the *Principes* expand on the ideas presented in the earlier book. Such is the chapter on the use of statistics in medicine. One new section is a draft of a historical survey of medicine from antiquity to Bernard's own times. The discussion of vitalism is considerably more extended in the *Principes*.

One may perhaps make the same remark about the *Principes* as has sometimes been made about the *Pensées* of Pascal. Finished, it might well have lost some of the spontaneity of the parts we possess. Lest I be misunderstood, it must be admitted that Bernard's style has none of the brilliance of Pascal. But there is a quality of homely sincerity marking some pages of the *Principes* which makes it a fascinating study for the reader already familiar with the other writings. He sees, as it were, the author's mind dashing off at intervals on speculative tangents, and as often being pulled back to the topic at hand. The author returns irrepressibly to such questions as the relation between science and metaphysics. The problem of free will and determinism makes its way into a discussion of physiological investigation. There are many such passages which will call for comment in later chapters.

Most of the posthumous publications have one thing in common: they all manifest a strong interest on Bernard's part in broader philosophical questions. This is true of the *Pensées, Notes détachées* edited by Delhoume.[45] It is especially true of the little book entitled *Philosophie* made up of notes on Tennemann's *History of Philosophy* and on Comte's *Cours de philosophie positive*.[46] There are references here and in the *Principes* to an exposition of the topic *Sentiment et raison pure*, which bring up a tantalizing problem in regard to Bernard's unpublished papers. Dr. Delhoume, in a letter to the writer, reports having made a fruitless search for it. One is reduced to conjecture on the exact nature of the piece, but the following quotations suggest that it must have been a well-advanced treatment of some basic philosophical themes.

One passage expresses a sort of philosophical relativism. The reality of things consists in their relations: "C'est dans le *rapport* que se trouve l'*absolu*. C'est là le seul point de départ philosophique et scientifique suivant moi. Or ce rapport peut s'exprimer en nombre et la certitude devient définitive. L'absolu de ce rapport devient un axiome c.-à-d. une sensation d'évidence à laquelle il faut toujours remonter. Voy. *Sentiment et raison pure.*"[47] ("It is in the *relationship* that the *absolute* is found. That is the only point of departure for science and philosophy in my opinion. Now this relation can be expressed numerically and certainty is attained. The absoluteness of this relation becomes an axiom, that is to say an evidential sensation to which we must ever return. See *Sentiment and Pure Reason.*") Other fragments suggest a Pascalian intuitionism: "Le sentiment est un guide plus sûr. (S. et r. p.)"[48] ("Sentiment is a surer guide.") "Tout se réduit à un sentiment. Voyez ce que j'ai dit du sentiment et raison pure."[49] ("Everything reduces to a sentiment. See what I have said of sentiment and pure reason.") "Ce n'est pas la tête, c'est le cœur, c.à d. le vague l'inconnu qui mène le monde. Voir Sentiment et raison pure."[50] ("It is not the head but the heart, that is, the vague, the unknown which moves the world. See *Sentiment and Pure Reason.*") The piece seems to have included a refutation of Comte: "The great objection that I have against him is that he would suppress the moral and sentimental side of man. . . . What was true within certain limits becomes false when carried to excess and then everything becomes absurd. That will all be found explained in my *Sentiment and Pure Reason.*"[51] Another allusion testifies that Bernard had come to grips with the problem of free will and determinism: "Nous sommes fatalement libres, c'est à dire d'une manière nécessaire (dans le *Sentiment et raison pure*)."[52] ("We are fatally free [or fated to be free], that is, in a necessary manner. In the *Sentiment and Pure Reason.*") What was the fate of this mysterious work? Did the author dispose of it because he felt unsatisfied with it, or did his family destroy it out of fear of its possibly unorthodox religious character? Perhaps we shall never know, but we may conclude from these references to it that it would have been a precious testimonial of Bernard's philosophical preoccupations.

CHAPTER TWO

Bernard's Relation to Philosophical Traditions

THERE HAVE BEEN almost as many attempts to link Bernard to particular philosophical schools as there have been authors to write about him. The interpretations range from the common one which makes of him a Positivist to those which present him as a materialist, an idealist, even a Thomist unaware. Passages can be offered to support almost any one of these descriptions. The divergencies arise from differences of emphasis and omission on the part of the commentators, sometimes motivated by their private preferences and even showing signs of special pleading. To avoid such one-sidedness, one must try to define his philosophical patrimony. This can be accomplished through an examination of the numerous allusions made by Bernard to well-known philosophers.

It must be recognized at the outset that Bernard lacked the early philosophical training which might have enabled him to

27

formulate his views with more terminological precision. A colla-
tion of the various ways in which he uses the word *métaphysique*
would reveal a singular degree of vagueness. Sometimes he em-
ploys it as virtually synonymous with *théorique,* e.g., "Quand on
raisonne sur ses connaissances c'est la métaphysique."[1] ("When
one reasons about his knowledge, that is metaphysics.") A like
meaning is involved here: "L'interprétation du fait est quelque
chose de *métaphysique.*"[2] The interpretation of the fact is
metaphysical in character.") A different meaning is found elsewhere: "Le métaphysique quoique réel en tant qu'il est nécessaire à notre esprit reste complètement en dehors de nos moyens
d'action."[3] ("The metaphysical though real in so far as it is
necessary for our mind remains completely outside our means of
action.") In partial contradiction to this statement but retaining
the same usage of the word, he writes in the *Notes détachées:*
"Le physique agit sur le métaphysique (l'engendre-t-il? ou le
modifie-t-il?) mais jamais le métaphysique n'agit sur le physique."[4] ("The physical acts on the metaphysical [does it engender it? or does it modify it?], never does the metaphysical act on
the physical.") A similar meaning seems to be implied in a critical reference to Auguste Comte: "Jamais la métaphysique ne
disparaîtra: c'est encore une erreur de la philosophie positiviste."[5]
("Never will metaphysics disappear. That is another error of the
Positivist philosophy.") Again he declares at one point: "Nous
dirons avec Descartes: on pense métaphysiquement mais on vit
et on agit physiquement."[6] ("We say with Descartes: one thinks
metaphysically, but one lives and acts physically.") Still another
statement runs: "L'art est un arrangement idéal. L'art est du
métaphysique avec quelque chose d'indéterminé de non science
encore."[7] ("Art is an ideal arrangement. Art is metaphysical in
character, with something in it that is undetermined, not yet
science.") Obviously one must be cautious in interpreting any
text containing the word. Perhaps the meaning "extra-physical"
or "non-physical" is, in general, the safest to assume. Like the
Aristotelian source for the word, it has led Bernard's critics and
doubtless at times Bernard himself into confusion.

These citations suggest that if Bernard must be linked with
an earlier philosophical tradition, it is the Cartesian rather than

any other. The Cartesian dualism enabled him to pursue his scientific investigations while waiving the metaphysical questions which might arise. The esteem he had for Descartes was partly owing to the fact that, unlike many speculative thinkers, Descartes was also a productive scientist. The only true philosophers, he wrote once, are scientists.[8] In one of the private notes published by Dr. Léon Delhoume, Descartes is given a central place: "All the great philosophers have been materialists and idealists at the same time. Descartes is as mechanistic as he can be . . . but alongside this mechanism Descartes places the soul which is independent, and thus he becomes the ancestor of all modern idealism."[9] A passage from another notebook exhibits a marked wavering in the use of terms, but it is evidently a corollary development of the thought just quoted:

> To act one must be a materialist; for one can act only on matter.
> To understand, *think,* and believe one must be an idealist; for matter alone explains nothing.
> In other words, to *act* one must be an empiricist. To *understand,* one must be a theorist.[10]

The dualism manifested here is a tendency frequently exhibited in Bernard's personal notes as well as in some published writings. It is the source of many of the ambiguities in his philosophical remarks. It served the purpose of a *modus vivendi,* a way of living with philosophical perplexities, and a protective shield for his biological investigations. Yet was it not, from another point of view, an encumbrance on his development, the dead husks left from a chrysalis which he never completely shed? His originality as a thinker appears when he transcends the dualism, but it is a heritage which he never entirely abandoned.

His physiology was, in a sense, a fulfilment of Cartesian mechanism.[11] It continues the current leading from the Beast-Machine through La Mettrie's Man-Machine, Diderot's naturalism and Lavoisier's biochemistry to Cabanis and Magendie. The other, the spiritualistic side, of the Cartesian ontology provided him only with those sprigs of second-hand idealism which are dispersed through his writings, but which never bore fruit in the form of fresh insight or discovery. What he rendered unto

the Caesar of mechanism came back a thousandfold, what he
rendered unto Spirit was as good as lost. Lost, except for those
idealists who seize upon these phrases as evidence for their own
Weltanschauung.

His respect for Descartes is greater than for any other philosopher. A striking instance of this esteem is the comparison
with Francis Bacon set forth in the *Introduction*. The importance
of this comparison for Bernard is indicated by the fact that a
similar passage occurs in the posthumous *Principes de médecine
expérimentale*.[12] Carried away by Joseph de Maistre's polemical
assault, he could not arrive at a judicial estimate of Bacon's
position in the history of scientific thought. Yet he convinced one
noted critic, Ferdinand Brunetière, who thought Bernard had
demolished Baconian induction.[13] Bernard's paragraph on Bacon
is preceded by a warning against the dangers of the scholastic
and systematizing spirit when it is allowed to dominate science.
Only the experimental study of nature can enable one to understand what science really is: "Philosophy, which I consider ex-
cellent gymnastics for the mind, has in spite of itself systematic
and Scholastic tendencies which become harmful for the scientist
strictly so-called. Moreover, no method can replace the study of
nature which makes the true scientist."[14] The strictures which
follow on Bacon should be considered in this context:

> I do not believe . . . that there is a great advantage in
> discussing the definition of induction or deduction. . . .
> Yet Baconian induction has become famous, and it has
> been made the foundation of all scientific philosophy.
> Bacon was a great genius and his idea of the great res-
> toration of sciences is sublime . . . Bacon sensed the
> sterility of Scholasticism and clearly understood and an-
> ticipated the whole importance of experiment for the
> future of science. Nevertheless Bacon was not a scientist
> and did not at all understand the mechanism of ex-
> perimental method. It suffices to mention the unhappy
> attempts he made. Bacon recommends fleeing from hy-
> potheses and theories; but we have seen that they are
> the auxiliaries of method, as indispensable as scaffolding
> is for building a house.[15]

He espouses the inexact but commonly held view that Bacon was opposed to all use of hypotheses.[16] On this basis he presents in contrast the more fruitful contributions of Descartes: "When Descartes begins with universal doubt and repudiates authority, he gives precepts much more useful for the experimenter than those which Bacon gives for induction. We have seen that it is doubt alone which provokes the experiment. . . ." Bacon was wrong to make a fundamental difference between induction and deduction. As Bernard phrases it in his *Principes:* "Induction is . . . an uncertain, provisional syllogism, whose conclusion must be verified by experiment."[17] In his own experimental practice of which he cites various examples, Bernard cannot accept as valid the sharp distinction between induction and deduction which he imputes to Bacon.

He is unjust to Bacon in failing to acknowledge that the Englishman was censuring, not all hypothesis, but only the cobweb spinning of mediaeval Scholasticism. What can only be called a touch of animus against Bacon may have a partial explanation in a point which many commentators have missed. The role which he assigns to Bacon is rather similar to that which he attributes to Comte. It is evident from his notebook on the *Cours de philosophie positive* that he associates Bacon and Comte in his mind, and is unable to suppress a certain resentment at their pretentions to legislate over the sciences. Thus in a "Reflection on the first lesson of the positive philosophy," he assails Bacon as "une trompette et crieur public" who only repeated the scientific truths that were being discovered by the real experimental scientists, the Galileos and Torricellis.[18]

But if Bernard considers Descartes' methodological doubt more useful than Bacon's program, Descartes himself could err by failing to follow his own rules. A passage from the *Leçons de pathologie expérimentale* offers such a critique of Descartes as a physiologist:

Approaching the study of experimental sciences, Descartes brought to them the same ideas which had served him so well in philosophy. He proceeded in physiology as he had in metaphysics; he set up a philosophical principle to which he reduced the scientific facts, instead of starting from the facts and linking ideas to them *a posteriori,* ideas which would be only a kind of translation of the facts. The result was that although he took account of the physiological experiments known in his time, Descartes set forth a physiology which was really imaginary.[19]

The reference to Descartes' success in philosophy is ambiguous but worth noting. Bernard's letters to Mme Raffalovich repeatedly mention his study of Descartes.[20] He does not indorse Descartes *en bloc,* but neither does he dismiss him as a mere speculator. He does not follow the stereotype of Descartes the rationalist opposed to Bacon the empiricist. There is a statement in the *Introduction* which even Dr. Delhoume has supposed gives Descartes too much credit: "When Descartes said that one should rely only on the evidence or on what is adequately demonstrated, that meant that one must no longer rely on authority, as the Scholastics had done, but take one's stand only on the facts well established by experience."[21] Bernard could say this with perfect justice of a philosopher who, while capable of errors in physiology, was far from neglecting the function of experiment in science. The imprint of Cartesian thought is marked in the *Introduction*—nowhere more so than in what Bernard calls the criterion *par excellence,* the principle of experimental determinism joined with philosophic doubt.[22]

Other seventeenth-century thinkers who influenced him were Pascal and Leibniz. Although Pascal precedes Leibniz chronologically, it is more convenient to discuss the latter first, both because of the historical bond between Descartes and Leibniz and because Bernard often thought of them together. Pascal, on the other hand, is linked with problems falling outside of that context. Bernard's interest in Leibniz does not embrace the areas in which modern philosophers like Bertrand Russell have descried the marks of that prolific genius. Bernard's Leibniz is the historically familiar proponent of the pre-established harmony. The concept is clearly implied in the basic distinction which Bernard makes between the physical and the biological sciences: ". . . the physicist and the chemist can reject any idea of final causes in the facts which they observe; whereas the physiologist is led to admit a pre-established and harmonic finality in the organism, for its partial activities are interdependent, one activity engendering another."[23] The phrases are reminiscent of Leibniz; the idea, however, is essentially the Aristotelian entelechy. Elsewhere Bernard seems to indorse Leibniz's doctrine of psychophysical parallelism: "Here we must separate the metaphysical world from the physical world which serves as its foundation, but which is self-sufficient. Leibniz expressed this delimitation in words we cited at the beginning of our article; science sanctions it today."[24] In the beginning of the article, Bernard compares Leibniz and Descartes from this angle:

> Descartes gave a metaphysical definition of the soul and a physical definition of life. The soul is the superior principle manifested in thought, life is only a superior effect of mechanical laws. The human body is a machine formed of springs, levers, canals, filters, sieves, and presses (i.e., such as oil presses). This machine exists for itself: the soul joins it merely to contemplate as a spectator what takes place in the body, but in no way does it intervene in the vital function. From the physiological point of view, the ideas of Leibniz are very analogous to those of Descartes. He also separates the soul from the body, and although he supposes a concordance between them pre-established by God, he denies them any sort of reciprocal action. "The body," he says, "develops mechanically, and mechanical laws are never violated in natural motions: everything happens in the soul as if there were no body, and in the body as if there were no soul."[25]

It would doubtless be an error to conclude from this passage that Bernard is in fact a Leibnizian. Leibniz simply supplies him with a useful defense against vitalism. Yet it is more than a maneuver in the strategy and tactics of the war of ideas. Bernard is disposed to favor dualistic views, but he is perhaps too complaisant to trouble overmuch about theoretical distinctions in matters of speculative philosophy, unless the distinctions entail consequences for his scientific practice.

Bernard is more negative in regard to Leibniz's concept of determinism, as well as the theory of the monad, and the treatment of philosophy *de more geometrico*. He denies the proposition that necessary truths are innate, and rejects the idea that philosophy must be treated rationalistically, in accordance with the method of demonstration, like mathematics. "Il n'y a pas de rationalisme, tout est expérimental."[26] Tennemann formulates Leibniz's opinion as follows: "There are certain necessary truths . . . belonging to Metaphysics as well as to Mathematics, the certainty of which cannot be ascertained by Experience, but must be sought within the Soul itself."[27] Against this position, Bernard asserts the superiority of intuition coupled with experiment. There seems to be an echo of Pascal in his rebuttal: "La raison ou le raisonnement seuls sont la source de toutes nos erreurs. Le sentiment est un guide plus sûr. Dans les mathématiques le sentiment de l'évidence est toujours le point de départ, mais on peut faire l'expérience si l'on veut."[28] ("Reason or reasoning [taken] alone is the source of all our errors. *Sentiment* is a surer guide. In mathematics the *sentiment of* evidence is always the point of departure, but one can make the experiment if he wishes.") As for the windowless monad, it is a notion in which Bernard, as an experimental scientist, can have little interest. He rejects the idea of the self-activity of matter. A monad must be stimulated from outside in order to manifest its properties.[29] More important for Bernard than the monad is Leibniz's determinism. Here Bernard encounters a good deal of difficulty. As Lalande notes, he does not seem to have completely understood Leibniz's thought.[30] Thus we may read in the *Principes:* "Knowledge and liberty exist in man. But nevertheless, if everything is not preordained, as Leibniz thought, everything is fixed in the laws of a necessary determinism."[31] He differentiates his scientific or experimental determinism from the philosophical determinism of Leibniz, and goes so far as to denominate the latter as "fatalism." He evidently misses the distinction between logical necessity and hypothetical contingency by means of which Leibniz refutes fatalism and leaves a place for freedom. One may conclude that Leibniz exerted less influence on Bernard than did Descartes. The physiologist found in his writings terms like the pre-established harmony which he utilized without rigorous exactitude. And Leibniz's conception of necessity undoubtedly helped him to clarify his thinking on determinism, even though he did not clearly grasp the German philosopher's position.

One motive for Bernard's interest in Leibniz was his greatness as a mathematician. Does not Bernard often say that the only true philosophers are scientists? To gain his attention, it seems that a philosopher must first present credentials showing him to be a scientist also. The possession of such credentials certainly enhanced the appeal for him of that other seventeenth-century thinker, Pascal. The latter's barometrical investigations are used in the *Introduction* to illustrate the nature of scientific observation and experiment.[32] But Pascal's influence goes deeper than that. Bernard pays tribute to both Descartes and Pascal for their refusal to submit to the authority of the past. The experimental sciences, in particular, can only advance by revolution and by the absorption of old truths into a new form. Bernard echoes Pascal's famous remark on the growth of knowledge:

> If every great man pushes the science he enriches a long step forward, no great man has ever claimed to set its final limits. He is destined by necessity to be surpassed. . . . Great men have been compared to giants carrying pygmies on their shoulders who see farther than they. That means that sciences progress, and precisely because of the influence of great men.[33]

But Pascal, after all, had found this thought already expressed by mediaeval writers. He exerted an individual appeal for Bernard which is more personal and in some ways more significant than anything which Bernard could respond to in Descartes.

It is interesting that this influence worked against that excessive form of rationalism which Leibniz appeared to represent. We have quoted above Bernard's denial of philosophical truths whose certitude rests not on experience but must be based in the soul itself: "Reason taken alone is the source of all our errors. Feeling (sentiment) is a safer guide." Though Bernard's reaction to Leibniz is couched in terms reminiscent of the *Pensées* of Pascal, he is thinking, not of religious truth, but of scientific method. The notebook cited is a record of studies and reflections made at the time he was preparing the *Introduction*. *Sentiment* here means the intuition or insight which comes to the mind of the scientist faced with a problem to be solved. Scientific research also requires the *esprit de finesse* which Pascal opposed to the *esprit de géométrie*. A fragment from an unpublished notebook of 1877 links this point specifically to Pascal: "What is a *fact?* Deduction and induction are the same thing. But deduction is easy. It is the *esprit géométrique*. Induction is much more difficult, it requires a sure and steady mind. It is the *esprit de finesse* of Pascal."[34] One may compare in this connection a passage from the *Introduction* which brings out clearly the danger of the "geometric" approach in biology: "This overconfidence in reasoning, which leads a physiologist to a false simplification of things, results on the one hand from ignorance of the science of which he speaks, and on the other hand from a lack of feeling for the complexity of natural phenomena."[35] Like Pascal, Bernard possessed a keen sense of this complexity, without succumbing to the former's distrust of reason. Bernard would never follow Pascal in writing "against those who delve deeply into the sciences, like Descartes."[36]

Bernard returns again and again to Pascal's penetrating critique of doctrinaire rationalism. Thus in his discussion of the question "What is life?" he is reminded of Pascal's *aperçu* that certain fundamental terms cannot be defined:

> Pascal, who knew so well all the weaknesses and illusions of the human mind, remarks that in reality true definitions are only creations of our minds, that is, *definitions of names,* or conventions for shortening discussion; but he acknowledges basic or primordial words that we understand without having to define them.
>
> Now, the word *life* is one of them.[37]

While preparing his Muséum lectures of 1877, Bernard comes back to the subject. Now he associates the conception of Pascal with the ideas of the mathematician Poinsot: "Poinsot did not want people to define time, space, or life. These are, he said, primary ideas which one does not define. Pascal also believes that we do not define anything. A definition is only a convention."[38] Pascal confirms Bernard in his belief that the study of life must be approached with a mind free from presuppositions or *a priori* definitions. One does not embark on an investigation of vital phenomena with a preconceived definition of life. In his campaign against dogmatists in science, whether vitalists or mechanists, Bernard was able to look for support and stimulation in certain *Pensées* of Pascal.

There is a more intimate way in which the presence of Pascal makes itself felt in some of the writings of Bernard. Yet Dr. Pierre Mauriac certainly goes too far in attributing to Bernard the religious anxiety of Pascal. If Bernard is religious in any sense, it is as a seeker after truth and never as a seeker of salvation. The torment of the unknown of which he writes in the concluding chapter of the *Introduction* has nothing in common with the dread of Judgment. The ardent desire for knowledge is the single motive which spurs on the investigator in his endeavors. It is this knowledge which he grasps at and which nevertheless continues to fly before him which becomes at the same time his only torment and his only happiness:

> But by a caprice of our nature, this joy of discovery so sought after . . . vanishes as soon as it is found. It is only a flash whose light has uncovered for us other horizons towards which our unslaked curiosity urges us yet more ardently. As a result, in science too the known loses its charm, whereas the unknown always allures us. . . . That is the feeling expressed by Pascal in a perhaps paradoxical form when he says: "We do not seek things, but the quest."[39]

Where Bernard parts company with Pascal is in the application which he makes of the idea. For Bernard science is not a *divertissement*, an evasion of more crucial issues. The scientist does find truth, only in fragments, to be sure, but there is a continuous, if gradual, progress towards an ever more complete understanding of nature. Unlike the Sisyphus of the legend, the scientist does advance.

The topic is frequently in Bernard's mind. Aside from an identical passage in his article "Du Progrès dans les sciences physiologiques," there exist in his notebooks at least two drafts of the same thought. Here he gives it a more skeptical expression than in the confident pages of the *Introduction*. In the version published in Delhoume's edition of the *Principes,* the writer develops it in a direction very different from the other book. Indeed the style and purport are such as would certainly have excluded it from the *Principes* had he been able to finish this treatise. In an earlier chapter we have already offered evidence that his plan for the *Principes* lacked definiteness. So much is but a rewording, if not a *pre-wording,* of material in the *Introduction.* And so much belongs outside of the proper scope of either the *Introduction* or the *Principes.* Such is the character of the passage before us. It belongs in a different book, in some collection of philosophical reflections like the *Pensées, Notes détachées,* or *Le Cahier rouge.* The imprint of Pascal on his meditations is deeper than one would suppose from a reading of the *Introduction:*

> Man, as Pascal says, seems made rather for the quest for truth than the knowledge of this absolute truth . . . If man could have the absolute knowledge he seeks, it is likely that he could no longer live, that he would commit suicide through boredom. I do not know whether our yearning for the truth is a sign that we will know it; but it is certain that we can never possess it on this earth.[40]

The mood of agnosticism, and the suggestion of yearning for some transcendental truth, are both in contradiction with the parallel passage of the *Introduction.* The author even touches on the perils of knowledge, a motif which is to be one of the stereotypes of tender-minded thought later in the century: "Our mind . . . has a thirst for seeking knowledge, but if it found what it seeks, it would be consumed and destroyed."[41] It is a modern variation on the theme of the fruit of the tree of knowledge. But this seems to be only a momentary mood for Bernard. He feels no temptation to follow Pascal in his flight from science.

It is evident that Bernard was profoundly impressed by the writer of the *Pensées.* He read Pascal repeatedly in the last decade and a half of his life. Pascal provided him not only with arresting ideas for philosophical meditation, but also with sharp insights useful in his scientific work. Pascal was for him an ally against dogmatism, in particular against the doctrinaire rationalism which both called the "esprit de géométrie."

Leaving behind the "Century of Genius" and passing on to the eighteenth century, we are struck by the paucity of references to the great figures of the Enlightenment. The only French thinkers he mentions are Buffon, Condillac, and Diderot. He welcomes Buffon as an ally against the "esprit de système." He rejects Condillac's view that a science must start out with a perfect language.[42] More important for him is Diderot. He was interested enough in him to undertake a study on Diderot and medicine, in collaboration with the young Georges Barral. Unfortunately time ran out on him, and the paper was left unfinished upon his death. Diderot's conception of the experimental method, and such writings as his *Physiological Notes,* did not have the influence upon Bernard's development that they might have had if he had encountered them earlier. A full realization of the value of Diderot's ideas on these topics was only beginning to be reached at the time of Bernard. One feels certain that Bernard's study would have furthered the appreciation of Diderot as a scientific thinker.[43]

One of the works annotated by Bernard while preparing to write his *Introduction* was the *History of Philosophy* published by Tennemann, a follower of Immanuel Kant. This circumstance may partly explain the fact that Bernard's treatment of philosophical topics sometimes assumes a Kantian coloration. To what extent did he accept the Kantian system so popular with his contemporaries like Paul Janet and Charles Renouvier? In order to answer this question we must differentiate between what is specifically Kantian and what Kant shares with other thinkers. There is something in common between Kant and Descartes, and Bernard does not always distinguish between them. On the other hand, there are broad resemblances between Kant and the Positivists, and one must be careful not to ascribe to direct Kantian influence something which is a part of the climate of ideas during the time of Bernard.

The common element between Kant and Descartes is that of rationalism. In the *Introduction,* Bernard sets down the principle: "In the experimental method as in everything else, *the only real criterion is reason."* He opposes this principle to the worship of "facts" of the empiricists, who do not realize that a "fact" may be pointless unless it is part of an idea or theory. The words he italicizes are linked with Kant in his *Leçons de pathologie expérimentale:* "Truth cannot be illogical: everything true is necessarily rational, everything goes back finally to reason, the only criterion according to Kant."[44] Now it hardly seems necessary to invoke Kant in support of this typically Cartesian standard. Elsewhere he fails to mark the difference between Kant and Leibniz. He is vague on what is original in Kant's theory of knowledge. In his notes on Tennemann, like any empiricist, he refers all knowledge to experience and denies validity to *a priori* truths: "They are, in my opinion, only uncertain attributes, if not nullities." In another notebook, he appears to impute to the Critical Philosophy a tenet which Kant had been at pains to disown. Bernard does not distinguish between the categories and the body of factual knowledge. How else are we to understand these words of his *Cahier rouge?* "There is no knowledge existing outside or above experience, as Kant thinks. All knowledge is of experience."*[45] Bernard has fallen into a common misinterpretation which has been recently described by Henry D. Aiken as follows: "Casual readers are sometimes led to suppose that Kant was attempting to provide a mode of access to things that are literally 'out of this world.' They are mistaken. Kant had, in fact, very stringent views about the possibility of our knowing any transcendent reality whatever."[46] Bernard does not recognize the novel character of the Copernican Revolution which Kant instituted against his rationalistic forerunners Descartes and Leibniz.

The point in common between Kant and the Positivists, taken in a broad sense, is their denial of metaphysics. Knowledge of the essence of reality, of the Thing-in-Itself, is impossible. All we can know is phenomena. Bernard is in general accord with this position. His formulations of his outlook provide no warrant for inferring that he is any closer to Kant than he is to Positivism. Typical of his statements are the following taken from the *Introduction:* "Since the essence of things must always remain un-

---

*"Il n'y a pas de connaissances qui soient hors ou au-dessus de l'expérience comme le veut Kant. Elles sont toutes expérimentales." I have taken a liberty with the word *expérimentales,* which translated literally would certainly be too narrow.

known to us, we can know only the relations between these things, and phenomena are only the results of these relations." And again: "The condition of existence of a phenomenon can tell us nothing of its nature."[47] Bernard occupies a spot in the geography of ideas which marks the point of intersection between Kant's notion of the Ding-an-Sich, Comte's Positivism and Herbert Spencer's concept of the Unknowable. It is Dubois-Reymond's *Ignorabimus*. The concordance is a sign of the times.

A more specific correspondence with Kant has been proposed by Abel Rey, with regard to the so-called *idée directrice* employed by Bernard to describe the unity of the living organism. Biological phenomena appear to follow a plan, a guiding and creative "idea." It is an error to imagine that this idea is active in the manner of a physical force. Bernard stated in his essay on "La Définition de la vie": "This conception does not move out of the intellectual domain to react on the phenomena for the explanation of which the mind had created it." Rey finds this reminiscent of one of the conceptions expounded by Kant in his *Critique of Judgment*. One must be guided by the principle of purpose or final cause, even though this principle is but a convenient fiction and has only a subjective value. It does not depend so much upon the nature of the object to which it is applied as on our need to explain the phenomenon. Without being a constituent concept of our understanding or our reason, it can serve as a regulative concept, or as a guiding thread, for our reflective judgment in its study of the natural world, by a remote analogy with our own causality, our own purposiveness. The resemblance between Bernard's and Kant's statements is striking. Here Bernard goes farther than the cognate Spinozist idea which he indorses in one of his other writings: "There is no need to show at length, that nature has no particular goal in view, and that final causes are mere human figments."[48] Unfortunately Bernard's various statements on the *idée directrice* lack the rigor and precision which would enable us to determine whether he stood closer to Kant or to Spinoza. Even the ghost of Aristotle's entelechy comes in to obscure his position.

What weakens any argument making Kant an important influence upon Bernard's thought is the fragmentary and negative character of the physiologist's allusions to the German philosopher. In his notebook on the *Cours de philosophie positive,* he includes Kant among the pure philosophers whom he compares unfavorably to scientists like Descartes, Leibniz, Newton, and Galileo: "Kant, Hegel, Schelling, etc., all that is hollow, and all their efforts combined have not given the slightest truth to the world."[49] In his published references, as we have seen, he is more respectful. On the whole, Kant played no decisive part in Bernard's evolution.

We have seen how Bernard sometimes echoes Kant, sometimes rejects him, not always for pertinent reasons. There is a puzzling passage in *Le Cahier rouge* which appears to be directed against some members of the Kantian succession like Fichte and Schelling: "Some say that knowledge is completely subjective. It is in the mind and not in reality. That is absurd. No doubt the form of knowledge as we conceive it is in our minds, but facts do exist."[50] Bernard appears to concede the validity of the Kantian categories while rejecting decisively any such idealisms as those of Berkeley and Fichte. Aside from the dualistic tendency which has already been commented upon in connection with Descartes, the fragment suggests the same train of thought often found in Bernard's brief speculations on mathematics: namely, that even mathematical truths would be different if the mind were differently constructed.[51] It is related to the idea of Buffon which Bernard approves, that it is the mind of man which imposes its classifications upon nature. Bernard does not, however, pursue this concept systematically. It serves him in practice as a *caveat* against premature generalizations, and not as a stepping-stone to any such conventionalist philosophy of science as that of Henri Poincaré.

Of the German thinkers of Kant's time and after, Goethe is the most important for Bernard. The occasional allusions to Schelling and Hegel are vague and largely insignificant.[52] There is reason for pausing momentarily over the name of Jacobi. Tennemann places "sentiment" at the center of Jacobi's thought:

> Jacobi was thus led to found all philosophy on belief, which he describes as an instinct of reason, a sort of knowledge produced by an immediate feeling of the

> mind, a direct apprehension without proof of the True and Supersensuous. . . . In the same manner Jacobi would found the principles of Morality upon Sentiment.[53]

It is this passage which Bernard summarizes in his notebook on Tennemann: "Jacobi fonde toute connaissance philosophique sur un sentiment, une croyance."[54] The comment is interesting because it shows him taking grist for his mill even from the religious idealism of Jacobi, a philosophy with which he has really nothing in common. Bernard has in mind something quite different from Jacobi when he writes: "Everything reduces to a *sentiment*. See what I have said of sentiment and pure reason." He is thinking of the role of *sentiment* or intuitive anticipation in scientific discovery. The fragment on Jacobi is rather typical of most of his references to philosophers. He is less interested in them for their own sake than in the application which he might make of them for his own philosophy of experimental science.

Like Descartes and Leibniz, Goethe could recommend himself to Bernard by virtue of being a scientist and not merely a speculative thinker. Bernard finds himself in agreement with Goethe on the function of experiment as a mediator between thought and reality. In fact, he cites Goethe's words more than once on this very point.[55] But he is suspicious of the generalizing tendency exemplified by Goethe's genetic conceptions. We are reminded of his repeated criticisms of the "generalizers" Bacon and Comte. In this instance, his criticism is directed specifically against what he regards as a form of the genetic fallacy:

> . . . Excessive generalization creates a purely ideal science which no longer is linked with reality. This danger, which is slight for the contemplative naturalist, becomes very great for the physician, who must above all look for objective and practical truths. Doubtless we cannot deny our admiration to those vast horizons caught sight of by the genius of Goethe, Oken, Carus, Geoffroy Saint-Hilaire, Darwin, in which a general conception shows us all living creatures as being the expression of types continually changing as organisms and species evolve, and in which every living creature individually disappears as but a reflection of the totality to which it belongs.[56]

Lumping together scientists like Darwin with such speculative thinkers as Oken points to a basic lack of sympathy with the theory of evolution. He seems reluctant to concede its validity, while raising here no determined objection to it. In the *Principes* he expresses the same reservations as in the *Introduction,* the same suspicion of broad generalizations in which significant individual differences are lost in a homogeneous haze:

> . . . if with Darwin we end up by arriving at a single species. . . . Are we not obliged to take account of everything that exists and is there anything else aside from individuals? . . . for the physician that is a very important point. . . . He is not the physician of the human type, of the human species. He is the physician of an individual.[57]

There is a delightful irony as well as a revealing human note of personal impatience in a later passage of the *Principes* in which he assails the genetic fallacy. Bernard sounds almost like an avatar of Cuvier re-enacting a part in the great debate of 1830 with Geoffroy Saint-Hilaire on unity and variety. Can he be aiming at Goethe's famous discovery of the intermaxillary bone and the work on the metamorphosis of plants? It would seem more likely that he is attacking contemporary opponents who invoke against him the names of those great thinkers Goethe and Darwin:

> There is a philosophical school which is an echo of the German Philosophers of Nature, which would have it that everything is found in everything else; the great sympathetic nerve and the spinal cord are the same thing; the pancreatic juice, the liver, have, in a word, nothing special about them. Nothing is special, everything is general. A leaf is a flower, and vice versa.[58]

Bernard admits that such generalizations have some philosophical value, but he emphasizes that they become false when applied in practice. This practical orientation partly explains his attitude toward Goethe and Darwin. Looked at from this experimental and medical perspective, Darwinism seems remote and speculative, because it appears to be neither susceptible of experimental verification nor applicable in medicine.

In his late work, *Leçons sur les phénomènes de la vie,* Bernard comes close to saying that the idea of evolution makes no difference for medicine or physiology: "In the present state of things, morphology is fixed . . . whatever may be our conception of the evolution which leads to it. Whether one follows Cuvier or Darwin matters little; they are two different ways of conceiving the history of the past . . . they provide no means of governing the future." According to Elie de Cyon, he expressed doubt that the Darwinians could explain by natural selection such marvelous mechanisms as the cardiac nerves.[59] The somewhat equivocal nature of these allusions to evolution tempts the reader to wonder whether there might not have been other motives for his standoffish attitude. He had evidently been provoked by invidious comparisons between his concentration on particular problems and the vast syntheses of Darwin.[60] With all his fairness and perspicacity, he unwittingly allowed his sensitiveness in the face of such criticism to affect his objectivity with regard to those wider aspects of biology which by their very nature could not be dealt with in his laboratory.

In this historical sketch and analysis of his philosophical heritage, we have now reached Bernard's own times. It is interesting to consider his relations with one of his contemporaries specializing in philosophy: Paul Janet, described by Émile Bréhier as a follower of Victor Cousin who sought to combine eclecticism with modern science.[61] In 1864 Janet sent Bernard a copy of his polemic against Ludwig Büchner and Darwin, *Le Matérialisme contemporain,* and the physiologist's acknowledgment shows that the gift was not ignored.[62] While we do not possess any clear evidence on Bernard's opinion of the little book, we do have available his comments on a later and more ambitious work by Janet. The latter's treatise *Les Causes finales* is an attempt to demonstrate the existence of final causes with the help of data from the natural sciences. For many of his illustrations the author draws upon the experimental discoveries of Bernard himself.[63] But though inclined to be conciliatory in his remarks on Janet's thesis, Bernard leaves no doubt about his own opinion:

The present function of organs is not the cause which determined their formation. M. Paul Janet has brought together all the arguments to prove that things are arranged, harmonized, with a view to a determined end. We agree with him, for without this harmony life would be impossible; but that is no reason for the physiologist to seek the explanation of morphology in final causes now active.

Using as an example the eye of the rabbit, Bernard denies that the final aim of receiving impressions of light had determined the structure and guided the formation of the eye: "We must protest against the abuse of this idea in physiology. The final cause does not intervene as a law of nature now present and active." Referring to the accidents which may put an end to the rabbit's growth, he exclaims: "It would be a very blind kind of foresight whose calculations were so often thwarted."[64]

The concept of final causes can have a meaning only in reference to a first cause, and the first cause is beyond the reach of human knowledge: "In my opinion, they blend in confusion at an unattainable remove." It belongs to speculative philosophy and not to science. Bernard cites Spinoza in support of his position: "Final causes do not indicate the nature of things, but only the make-up of the imaginative faculty." We recall what was said above regarding Kant. But Bernard does not follow this idea to its consequences. He remains content with agnosticism: "Any effort to explain the first cause of this vital plan takes us outside of science." There is for him no warrant except subjective preference for choosing among the various answers to the question of teleology: "Whether it is an *intelligent and provident intention,* as the finalists say, a *condition of existence,* as the positivists would have it, *a blind will,* according to Schopenhauer, or an *unconscious instinct,* as Hartmann puts it, that is a question of one's own feeling. . . ." Consistent with his usual stand, he consigns final causes to the metaphysical realm. He does concede a possible validity to a limited form of teleology: "As a philosophical physiologist, one can accept a kind of *particular finality,* or *intra-organic teleology.*" This is but another way of expressing the concept of organism, of the growth and interrelation of bodily organs. In practice the physiologist can only waive the question of morphological laws. The essential factor, heredity, is as yet too imperfectly understood to permit a more scientific answer.[65]

Thumbing through Janet's little book on contemporary materialism, Bernard might have noticed an allusion to the German philosopher Hermann Lotze (1817-1881), described as a physiologist who defends the idealist point of view. There is a striking parallel with certain statements of Bernard in Janet's description: "M. Lotze returns to Cartesian dualism and seems disposed to agree that the laws of life must be reduced to the laws of physics, chemistry, and mechanics; but he separates thought from the body, he grants to the soul alone the legislative power, and to the body the executive power."[66] In his *Principes,* Bernard uses the same turn of phrase: "There is in living beings the vital force which gives to them their development and form. This form is independent of matter; it is the *legislative power* which is above matter and directs it; but the *executive power* of this arrangement is entirely material and physicochemical."[67] One wonders how much Bernard may have read of Lotze, or talked of him with Mme Raffalovich. He was certainly aware of Lotze. Among the papers of Bernard at the Collège de France is a manuscript translation of the Lotzean Adolf Fick's *Compendium de physiologie de l'homme.*[68] In another connection as regards the typical Bernardian concept of the inner environment, there is found in the significantly titled *Microcosmos* of Lotze the following suggestive formulation: "Even the regularity of the circulation of the blood is, within wide limits, self-maintained, the amount of possible divergence being at the same time fixed." Lotze goes on to speak of "the comparative constancy with which, under the most various influences of food and life, the blood maintains or restores its normal composition."[69] The parallels are intriguing. Yet the catchwords on the legislative and executive forces are the only definite link, and Bernard could have got them from Janet.

Bernard's commentary on Janet's thesis of final causes is quite as dualistic as his remarks on Descartes. He continues to distinguish between the proper domain of science and the area of ultimate questions which belongs to metaphysics. Generally he describes the latter as insoluble, but he does not regard them as illegitimate or as destined to disappear with the progress of science. The division he preserves between phenomena and noumena differentiates him from the typical Comtean Positivist. In many ways, however, he is close to that philosophy. Just how close remains to be defined.

It is evident that Bernard had come, through reading and personal association, to possess a philosophical frame of reference. This frame of reference was not too firmly put together, perhaps, and some of the pieces were lacking. But it is impossible to treat him as a pure experimentalist like Magendie, with only a casual interest in philosophy. This fact has not always been made clear by those who have discussed his work. Dr. Pierre Mauriac, for example, is somewhat supercilious about his cultural background: "A few names of philosophers, of Descartes, Molière, of Pascal once, are the only traces of his culture."[70] One must not discount too sweepingly his general culture. His literary allusions include Rabelais, Montaigne, Boileau, La Fontaine, Fontenelle, Rousseau, Lamennais, and Musset.[71] He was a friend of such deeply cultured men as Renan, Sainte-Beuve, Mérimée, and Taine.[72] In the more restricted field of the philosophy of science, André Lalande saw fit to mention the infrequency of his references: "Claude Bernard belongs to the laboratory tradition, but of what is this tradition composed? . . . It has been said that the soil of science is fertile because it is the *cemetery* where lie the skeletons of philosophical systems."[73] One could say that the present chapter has been devoted to the exhumation of a few bones from these systems. But it is truer to say that Descartes and Pascal especially, remained very much alive for Bernard.

He never quite left behind the Cartesian dualism of body and spirit, even though the materialist side, in his physiology, overshadows pretty completely the idealistic side. In line with the Kantian philosophy, he tends to identify this dichotomy with that of phenomena and noumena. The most valuable legacy of Descartes to Bernard is, however, the rationalism, and above all, his methodological doubt. It is this which enabled Bernard to escape the empiricism which he had to guard against, as a pupil of Magendie. On the other hand, he found in Pascal a counterpoise to the excessive rationalism of Descartes, the *esprit de finesse* against the *esprit de géométrie*. It has been said that Kant sought a middle ground between the rationalism of Leibniz and the empiricism of Hume. In his own less systematic way, Bernard also strove for such a middle ground, and that is one of the main reasons why he consulted the philosophers. But unlike Kant, who erected on this middle ground an elaborate philosophical edifice, Bernard, always suspicious of systems, was content to set up his laboratory there.

CHAPTER Three

Claude Bernard
and Auguste Comte

BLURRING of the distinction between
the broad and the narrow meanings of the term "positivism"
has resulted in a tendency to make various thinkers into
mere disciples of Comte. In Bernard's case, the notion that he
lacked any real culture beyond the domain of natural science
has made it easy to suppose that he was merely a follower who
for reasons of vanity or opportunism maintained silence concerning his indebtedness to the chief of the Positivist school.[1] One
point made in the preceding chapter is that Bernard had links
with philosophical tradition that owe nothing to Comte. Renan
and Taine have also been listed in the Positivist movement, although they both clearly disassociated themselves from it. Taine,
for example, rejects categorically the agnosticism of Comte and
aligns himself decisively with Hegel.[2] If we take positivism in its
broad sense, as signifying the study of the relations between

49

phenomena, with the explicit avoidance of metaphysical questions, Bernard is as much a positivist as John Stuart Mill or Herbert Spencer, and by the same token more of a positivist than Taine. But the issue is positivism in its restricted sense of Comtism. In this discussion we shall designate Comtism by spelling Positivism with a capital, or by writing the French form *positivisme*.

Close disciples of the school, like Hillimand, have expressed their sense of grievance at Bernard's failure to give credit to the master in the formation of his views. Some readers have found it strange that he does not even mention Comte in the works he published. There are, of course, several transparent allusions to Positivism in the *Introduction*. Other allusions become plain when compared to the wording of his notebook on the *Cours de philosophie positive*. The various posthumous publications place us in a better position to understand his attitude. It is a fact that he makes no avowal of a debt to Comtism, and that he explicitly repudiates some of its basic tenets. He scoffs at Comte's self-given title of specialist in generalities. He sees Comtism arrogating to itself the supervision of the whole scientific movement from the lofty heights of philosophy. His comparison of Comte to the fly in La Fontaine's fable of "The Coach and the Fly" might well have stung the faithful to the point of exasperation: "The philosopher who is not a scientist is sterile and arrogant. He tries to appropriate all the accomplishments of the human mind, imagining like the fly of the coach that it is he who produces all the discoveries through the ideas he gives forth in regard to them."[3] In a letter to Mme Raffalovich he calls her unduly enthusiastic over Littré and "those narrow and empty conceptions which are decorated with the name of *positivisme*."[4] He attributes a certain undesirable trend in medical training to false ideas stemming from Comte on the progressive complexity of the sciences.[5] He notes an "elucubration" of Comte's on the feasibility of straightening the plane of the ecliptic.[6] He is certainly unfair, but we can perhaps understand the feelings of the experimenter when he emerges from the laboratory and reads the pennings of a closet philosopher laying claim to jurisdiction over the sciences. One may also suspect in Bernard a lack of awareness of how much the intellectual climate in which he lived actually owed to the *Cours de philosophie positive.*

The Positivist philosophy was one of the representative expressions of the spirit of the age. When it proclaimed that scientific truth requires verification by observation and experiment, when it asserted that men can learn only the laws of phenomena and never the essential nature of reality, it was affirming the same principles which guided Bernard and the other scientists in their researches. Bernard could only agree with Comte that human knowledge can attain the "how" but not the "why" of phenomena: ". . . experience teaches us . . . that we cannot go beyond the *how,* that is, beyond the proximate cause or the conditions of existence of phenomena."[7] But he felt no need of learning from Comte's precepts what many scientists and notably Newton had demonstrated in their practice.[8] He looked upon Bacon and Comte in the same light. Bacon had only repeated the scientific truths that were being discovered by Galileo and Torricelli: "It was necessary to leave Scholasticism and take up experience. Others had done it before him; he said it the loudest. . . . Comte repeats (after Bacon) that in positive philosophy one should give up first and final causes."[9] Such philosophers are only a function of their time, and though they perform a useful service in a forensic way, it is not for them to pre-empt the direction of the sciences, whose specific problems they are not qualified to grasp.[10] Those devoted followers of Comte who take umbrage at Bernard's reticence seem to have missed the point. They would perhaps have liked it less had Bernard published a bill of particulars. Reading his notebook on the *Cours de philosophie positive,* we are inclined to believe that he was actuated by a commendable discretion rather than by envy or motives of expediency when he refrained from spelling out in his publications the full details of his disagreement.

One of the differences concerns the famous law of the three stages of scientific development. Bernard denies that the positive stage will ever completely supplant the metaphysical, or even the theological. The human heart is so constituted that mankind will never be satisfied with the "how" but must always keep asking "why?" Only the rare individuals, scientists like Bernard, may content themselves with the knowledge of the relations between phenomena. And even for Bernard, there are moments when this is not enough. He tends to shift his stand on the ultimate questions of metaphysics. But there is a narrower and more technical issue separating him from Comte. With regard to the evolution of the sciences, the triad of belief, reason, and experiment set forth in the *Introduction* conforms quite nearly with Comte's three stages. The first period is religious, the second philosophical, and the third scientific:

> The human mind, in the different periods of its evolution, has passed successively through *sentiment, reason,* and *experience.* First, sentiment alone, imposing itself on reason, created the truths of faith, namely theology. Reason or philosophy, then becoming the master, produced scholasticism. Finally experience or experiment, that is, the study of natural phenomena, taught man that the truths of the external world are not found formulated in the first place either in sentiment or reason. These are only our indispensable guides. . . .
>
> It is in this way that through the natural progress of things there appeared the experimental method which sums up everything and which . . . supports itself in turn on the three legs of this fixed tripod: *sentiment, reason,* and *experiment.*[11]

Clearly inspired by Comte, Bernard's conception is as clearly not identical with that of his forerunner. Bernard shifts the emphasis from the products of each stage to the process, or mode, of inquiry. The experimental method does not discard the earlier modes as obsolete, but comprehends them in a higher synthesis. Bernard's conception thus appears as more dialectical than the somewhat mechanical scheme of Comte.

The triad has a bearing not only on the historical phases of the evolution of science but also on the procedure in a particular problem in experimental research. Sentiment and reason are not superseded by experiment but remain as necessary factors in the process of discovery. Sentiment provides a hint for a possible solution of the problem; the hint is formulated in rational terms, and is submitted to the test of experience. To cope with any problem, therefore, the scientist recapitulates, as it were, the same steps through which humanity has passed in its historical quest for truth. Sentiment and reason, misleading by themselves, find their fulfilment when validated by experimental proof and counterproof.

How closely does Bernard follow the three stages of Comte in his survey of the history of medicine? The historical sketch given in his *Principes de médecine expérimentale* provides an answer. He divides the development into three periods: the pre-scientific, the empirical, and the scientific. The pre-scientific era corresponds to the theological stage of Comte, specifically mentioned by Bernard.[12] But no place is left for a metaphysical period as such. This might seem inconsistent with the fact that a large part of Bernard's writing was devoted to a criticism of metaphysical notions like the Life Force. The existence of such fallacies does not, however, require the designation of a definite metaphysical period in medicine. Empiricism is a more characteristic trend. On the other hand, the last epoch, that of experimental medicine, matches pretty nearly the *état positif*. It is significant that in the historical field which interested him the most, Bernard does not consistently apply the ideas of Comte.

While there are real affinities between Comte and Bernard in their general scientific outlook, it is in the sphere of biology that their differences stand out most sharply. The comparison has a special value today when the experimentalism advocated by Bernard no longer needs defense. If a modern reader wonders why the physiologist felt called upon to expound it at such length, the lessons on biology in the *Cours de philosophie positive* may supply the justification. Bernard's critique as we might construct it from his writings would fall under three main counts. First is his indictment of the "specialist in generalities." Second is his charge that Positivism is, despite its disclaimers, a *system,* and, therefore, liable to hamper free scientific enquiry. Third is his rebuttal of the detractor of experimentation in biology. Passages from Comte and Bernard will be cited relevant to each point.

In his attempt to "take all knowledge for his province," Comte was led, by the extreme proliferation of modern science, to conceive a hierarchy which would subordinate the particular studies to the Positive philosophy. This was a well-meant effort to obviate the evils of specialization and to open channels of communication between the specialties. Comte recognized as did Bernard that there is an artificiality about the compartmentalization of knowledge.[13] Nature is interconnected, and it is we who dismantle it, because of its vastness and complexity, into the various "ologies" and "onomies." But in trying to correct this departmental confusion, Comte added still another department. We read in his first Lesson:

> It suffices to make one more great specialty, the study of scientific generalizations. Let there be a new class of *savants,* appropriately educated, who, without devoting themselves to the special cultivation of any particular branch of natural philosophy, will occupy themselves exclusively, by considering the different positive sciences in their present stage, with the exact determination of the spirit of each science, with the discovery of their relations and interlinking features, and, if possible, with the reduction of all the principles proper to each into a lesser number of common principles, in full consistency with the fundamental maxims of the positive philosophy.[14]

Now it is against this claim to hegemony over the special sciences that Bernard raises his strongest objection. Only by active research in a particular field can one understand what science is. There is no royal road to natural science. In his notebook on the *Cours de philosophie positive,* Bernard comments with some acerbity on the "philosophe positiviste." "He is a man, as Comte says himself, who specializes in generalities." Such philosophers are the modern heirs of Scholasticism. "They are men whose aim is to reason about everything in general and nothing in particular, because they have no special knowledge."[15] Bernard expands on this point in a noteworthy passage of his *Introduction:*

> One must have been trained and have lived in laboratories to appreciate the full importance of those details of investigative procedures of which the false scientists who call themselves generalizers are so often ignorant or scornful. Yet we will never arrive at truly fruitful and

illuminating generalizations on vital phenomena, unless we have experimented ourselves and stirred up in hospital, demonstration room, or laboratory the noisome, quivering soil of life.

There is no doubt that Bernard feels strongly about the subject, for he continues, in a more rhetorical style than is customary with him, to develop the comparison:

Someone has said somewhere that true science should be compared to a charming, flower-grown plateau that one can reach only after having clambered up its steep slopes and scratched his legs against the thorns and underbrush. If I were asked to make a comparison expressing my feeling about the science of life, I should say that it is a superb drawing room brilliant with light to which one has access only through a long hideous scullery.[16]

Bernard grants that specialization is inevitable in practice. Partition of the domain of experimentation is a useful and necessary thing, for scientists cannot all attain the same measure of technical proficiency in the handling of the instruments and procedures of the laboratory. But specialization does not justify splitting general theory from factual content, or, in other words, abstract principles from concrete data:

I believe as a matter of fact that making one's specialty of generalities is an antiphilosophical and antiscientific principle, even though it has been proclaimed by a modern philosophical school which prides itself on being based on the sciences.[17]

Those who generalize can construct valid theories only if they are familiar with all the scientific details which these theories are designed to represent. The generalizations must be solidly grounded in particular facts: "The more deep-seated the detailed facts upon which they rest, the more stable will be the principles, just as a post is so much the firmer the deeper it is driven into the earth."[18]

The criticism which Bernard makes of Comte's "specialization in generalities" is of course related to the reproach he addresses against Positivism as a *system*. To indicate the sort of dogmatism Bernard has in mind, we may refer to certain passages in Comte's Lesson on biology, numbered 40: "Biological science must take a frankly speculative flight. . . ."[19] This goes counter to Bernard's insistence that what physiology needs is not theory but experimental data. Comte elaborates his thought in a direction which Bernard could hardly indorse, for the Lesson on biology urges a divorce between physiology and medicine:

> For physiology especially, our main endeavor today must be to separate it from medicine, in order to assure the originality of its true scientific character. . . . this overprolonged adherence to the art of medicine today impresses on physiological research a character of immediate and special application which tends greatly to narrow it down, and even to prevent it from acquiring the full generality it needs to take its due place in the system of natural philosophy. . . .[20]

While distinguishing between medical science and the profession of medicine, "this noblest of professions and most depressing of trades," Bernard cannot view the problem of physiology as independent from medicine: "Physiology and medicine must be blended and develop simultaneously and in parallel, for they are but one and the same science."[21]

The difference between Comte's speculative bent and Bernard's practical orientation is also illustrated in their approach to the problem of the nature of life. Comte's assertion that a philosophical conception of life is a prerequisite for biology seems, indeed, a violation of the spirit of positivism itself: "Since the study of vital laws constitutes the essential subject of biology, to form a precise idea of such an objective one must first analyze in itself the basic notion of *life,* seen from a philosophical point of view."[22] On the other hand, as we have already seen in connection with Pascal, Bernard questions the need of such a preliminary definition. There is a danger that the definition will become a fixed idea, misguiding the experimental scientist instead of helping him: "We must not, like the philosophers, set up an initial definition which we then consider an inviolable axiom. . . . In the sciences of life, so-called, one does not define, for one doesn't know what is being defined."[23]

Whether or not Bernard had Comte in mind in making these observations, the reference is explicit in the following passage, worth quoting at length because it is so expressive of the author's attitude in general:

> When the scientist pursues scientific investigation basing himself on any philosophical system whatever, he strays into regions too remote from reality, or else the system gives his mind a sort of deceptive confidence and rigidity in ill accord with the freedom and flexibility which the experimenter must always keep in his researches. One must therefore carefully avoid any kind of system, for the reason that systems are not found in nature, but only in the minds of men. Positivism, which repudiates philosophical systems in the name of science, has the same fault as they have of being a system. Now, in order to find the truth, the scientist has only to face nature and question it in accordance with the experimental method. . . . I believe that in this case the best philosophical system consists in not having any.[24]

In fact this whole concluding section of the final chapter of the *Introduction* can be read as a disavowal of Comtism and a rejection of its *ex cathedra* claim to regency over the sciences. The implication seems clear enough in these comments on the *entente cordiale* which Bernard believes should prevail between philosophy and science:

> Thus I do not accept the philosophy which would seek to assign limits to science. . . . Philosophy and science must not be systematic; they must join together without trying to dominate one another. . . . But if philosophy tried to enter the household of science and dictate to it dogmatically in regard to its products and methods of operation, then their agreement could no longer exist.[25]

Admittedly there were other schools besides Positivism against which these reproofs might have been directed. Comte was not the only philosopher who tried to assign limits to the sciences. But most of the others did not do this in the name of science. Comte did.

Doubtless Bernard was not thinking specifically of Comte's interdicts against Lamarckism, the study of the internal constitution of the stars, or even the cell theory.[26] The virtual ban on experiment which Comte imposed in the field of biology would be enough. This was one principle of Comte's program for biology which attacked the very foundations on which Bernard was to build his lifework. How does Comte state his objections to experimentation? To quote again from the Lesson on biology:

> In the study of living bodies, the nature of the phenomena seems to me to set up almost insurmountable obstacles to any broad and fruitful use of such a procedure; or at any rate, it is by methods of another type that the fundamental progress of biological science must above all be furthered.[27]

Among the methods which Comte thinks more suitable are the study of pathology and that of teratology, treated as observational sciences. Observation as against experiment is the keynote, also, of the comparative method, which Comte regards as the one best adapted to biology. Following Cuvier, Comte believes the life processes to be too delicate and spontaneous for the experimental approach. By its very essence, experimentation is disruptive of the subtle harmony inherent in the organism. Even to the extent that experimentation is applicable, it is better to change the environment than the living subject. But Comte is careful not to deny all merit to experiment. He is willing to recognize such contributions as that of Harvey on the circulation of the blood, that of Spallanzani on digestion, and others: "Despite this rigorous philosophical critique of the art of experiment as applied to physiological research, no one will infer, I hope, that I wish to condemn its use in biology absolutely." Yet that is faint encouragement. And he says again that this method is "far from being the general mode of exploration that is best adapted to the nature of biological phenomena." The phrases critical of experiment sound like a refrain through the prolix pages of the Lesson on biology: ". . . the lofty scientific objective of pathological exploration, conceived as offering biology, in a much more satisfactory manner, the true general equivalent of experimentation strictly so called. . . . The high and necessary superiority of pathological analysis over experimentation. . . . The direct mode is too disturbing and too abrupt."[28] Such statements might well justify placing Comte among the detractors of experiment so often adverted to by Bernard. This tendency of Comte did not pass unnoticed by a man who was later to become the outstanding supporter of Charles Darwin, Thomas Henry Huxley. As early as 1854, Huxley contrasts the model experimentalist Claude Bernard with the speculative philosopher Comte, citing the very passages we have quoted above.[29]

Bernard might almost be answering Comte's recommendation of pathological study over experiment in the following passage of the Introduction:

> . . . when it is a question of a science in its infancy, like medicine . . . the experimental idea does not always stand out clearly in such a vague subject. What then should be done? Should we abstain and wait until observations present themselves and bring us clearer ideas? We might often wait a long time and perhaps in vain. It is always worth while to experiment.[30]

Experimentation on living animals, and especially on those high in the scale, is beset with many problems and dangers that stem from the complexity of the subject. Often the experiment leads to disorders in the organism which mask, modify, or destroy the results sought. Bernard is as aware of these difficulties as Cuvier or Comte: "It is these very real difficulties which have marred experimental researches carried out on live animals, and have furnished arguments to the detractors of experiment." But science would never advance if one abandoned scientific methods because of their imperfection. The only thing to do is to improve them.[31]

We have discussed in an earlier chapter Bernard's reservations on the value of statistics in medicine. They might be compared with similar ideas put forward by Comte in the Lesson on biology. Comte rejects scornfully this so-called application of statistics to medicine:

> . . . this alleged application of what is called statistics to medicine, from which some scientists expect miracles, and which nevertheless could only lead to a profound and outright deterioration of the medical art, henceforth reduced to blind enumerations. Such a method, if we may call it by this name, would really be nothing but sheer empiricism, disguised under a vain mathematical appearance.[32]

But Bernard is less extreme than Comte. For the latter there are two obstacles preventing the application of mathematics to biology. One has to do with the complexity of biological phenomena. The other is more basic, for it involves an intrinsic impossibility of treating life in mathematical terms: ". . . any idea of numerical chemistry must become inapplicable to bodies whose molecular composition varies continually, for this variation is precisely what constitutes the fundamental characteristic of any living organism."[33] The same obstacles that confront the research physiologist become *a fortiori* even more insurmountable when the aim is quantitative as against qualitative knowledge. Bernard would agree with only the first of these reasons. Our present ignorance of vital phenomena makes premature the employment of mathematics in the organic realm, but we need not keep the door closed against mathematics on grounds of principle:

> It is not that I condemn the application of mathematics to biological phenomena, for it is only by that means that, in the future, the science will take shape; I simply have the conviction that the general equation is impossible for the moment, since the *qualitative* study of phenomena must necessarily precede their *quantitative* study.[34]

As for statistics, Bernard's position is more moderate than that of Comte. Statistics may be useful in the absence of definite knowledge, and they may point the way to more exact information. But medicine can never be scientific so long as it rests content with averages and probabilities.[35] There is a pronounced difference between this cautious view and the blanket condemnation quoted from the *Cours de philosophie positive*.

We possess no textual evidence to prove that Bernard was thinking of Comte in his allusions to the detractors of experiment in biology, of whom Cuvier was the most prominent.[36] As we have seen, Comte was not as categorical in his interdicts as was Cuvier. But it does not seem too much to say that Bernard's entire work was a refutation of Comte's program, and that this was fortunate for the progress of natural science. Bernard explicitly disavowed the "specialist in generalities," and warned against the danger that *positivisme*, like any system, might narrow the scope of investigation. Yet an impartial reader might wonder whether he was quite fair to Comte. Doubtless his attitude was affected by his aversion to the "Religion of Humanity" which he thought absurd.[37] Perhaps Comte's personal misfortunes contributed to Bernard's unfavorable judgment. Whatever all the reasons may be, Bernard's allusions to Comte are uniformly negative and critical. Though he found some truth in the Law of the Three Stages, he denied that mankind as a whole would ever accept the Positive Stage. Bernard's positivism, in so far as we can use the term at all, was limited to the domain of the physical and natural sciences, and did not extend to social or religious issues.

It has already been shown how the question of Bernard's affiliation with Positivism is complicated by the different meanings of the word. A mixture of these denotations and connotations seems to be involved in the following statement of Maurice Caullery:

> The physiology of Claude Bernard remains essentially *positive*. It studies and determines the conditions of the interrelationship of phenomena, without becom-

ing entangled in metaphysical preoccupations regarding their essence. Like so many other manifestations of French science in the XIXth century, it is therefore closely linked with the thought of Auguste Comte, who, in 1836, before Claude Bernard began his work, and perhaps under the influence of Magendie, had taken a stand against the vitalistic conceptions of Bichat, and had in his *Cours de philosophie positive,* with admirable prescience declared that the moment had come when Physiology should free itself not only from metaphysics but also from Medicine. That is what Claude Bernard carried out, in point of fact. . . .[38]

But the fact is Bernard did not respond to Comte's call for separating physiology from medicine. It was, to be sure, desirable to establish it as an independent science so that it could then with more authority take its rightful place as the foundation of medicine. That was Bernard's task. What Bernard always emphasized was the need, not for a separation, but for a union of physiology and medicine. This brings us to a significant difference of orientation between Comte and Bernard.

It is not by chance that Bernard begins his *Introduction* with the words "Preserve health and cure disease: this has been the problem of medicine from the beginning, and it is still looking for a scientific answer."[39] Comte inevitably followed a more speculative approach. Where Bernard starts with physiology and works outward, utilizing the other sciences as auxiliaries, Comte reviews the sciences *seriatim,* working in the direction of sociology. Both are moved by practical aims, but one is content with medicine and the other strives toward a science of society.

Though they share a utilitarian purpose, there is a sense in which Bernard is closer to the pragmatist position. Doubtless the mastery of nature is a leading motive in Positivism, as it is a dominant theme of Bacon's *Novum Organon.* But Comte's exposition of positive science does not generally go beyond the idea of verifiability. Bernard surpasses Positivism by the force and cogency with which he affirms that the final purpose of science is *action,* that the aim of all sciences can be stated in two words: predict and act. *Man can do more than he knows!* This is a germinal idea with a bearing for the philosophies of pragmatism and of Bergson. Yet, as Bernard realized, this concept of man as the "contremaître de la création" was not after all so far removed from Descartes, who proclaimed that men can use the powers of fire and air to make themselves the lords and proprietors of nature.[40]

There remains one further difference between Comte and Bernard. Precisely because the former lacked the experience of genuine research, he failed to recognize the importance of hypothesis. In this respect he can be linked with Bacon, who was taken to task by Bernard on this account. It is a curious fact that certain idealist contemporaries of Bernard, Paul Janet and Elme Caro, welcomed the physiologist as an ally against Comte, finding in the defense of hypothesis an argument against Positivism.[41] Nevertheless Bernard was closer to Positivism than to the Platonism which Caro and Janet read into his exposition of scientific method.

In this comparison of Bernard and Comte, I have tried to cast into relief the differences between them in philosophical outlook as well as in the specific area of biology. Bernard is a positivist only in a vague and general sense. His *proximate cause* is the same as the *condition of existence* of the Comteans. Both look for the how and not the why of phenomena. The physiologist adopted with some modifications the famous law of the Three Stages. But whereas Comte looks forward to the reign of the positive spirit in society and culture, Bernard limits its jurisdiction to the field of the sciences. Men will never cease asking the ultimate questions. In this respect Bernard is more traditional than Comte. But in another sense he is more modern than the leader of the Positivist school. Against Comte's speculative and generalizing tendency he asserts the need of concrete scientific work free from dogmatic intervention even in the name of a so-called scientific philosophy. It was this dogmatizing bent which induced Comte to set limits on the role of experiment in biology. While we do not know whether Bernard explicitly included him among the detractors of experiment, is it not evident that the entire career of the physiologist is a refutation of those detractors, Comte among them?

CHAPTER Four

Reactions to Three Key Ideas

UP TO NOW we have followed a chrono-
logical order in sifting out significant elements in Bernard's
philosophical heritage. Obviously he followed no such order
in the elaboration of his thought. His intellectual ontogeny
does not recapitulate the phylogeny of the historical succession
of philosophical ideas. We have, somewhat artificially, made a
historical projection of his own ideas, plotting them along the
axis leading from Descartes to Comte. This chapter will use a
horizontal coordinate instead of a vertical one, in an effort to
delimit his position by contrasting the divergent interpretations
made by his critics of certain key ideas. First will come the question of method, of the relationship between experimentation and
reasoning. Second, we shall take his conception of the physicochemical conditions of life. Related to this is the problem of
determinism. When we have seen that the concepts have in
Bernard's presentation a dual if not a dualistic character, it will

65

be easier to understand how the divergencies have arisen. Bernard himself remarked on this propensity of his readers:

> I have often noticed, for my part, that scientific facts I had presented were interpreted at the same time by vitalists and materialists as support for their opinions. But I must state that in carrying out my researches which have been thus appreciated, I had no intention of supporting either materialism or idealism, and still less of supporting both at the same time.[1]

Many a commentator has seized upon the element which seemed in harmony with his own beliefs and treated the opposite element as an inconsistency which Bernard should have removed. This inclination toward favoring one aspect over the other is especially evident in regard to his views on determinism and free will, and perhaps even more so with respect to his conception of the physics and chemistry of life. The question of scientific method has not called forth such sharply conflicting responses, but even in this connection examples of tendentious interpretation are to be found.

For Bernard, experiment and hypothesis are distinct but inseparable factors in scientific investigation. Where he differed most from his teacher Magendie was in the role he ascribed to reasoning, to a directing idea, in experimentation. Magendie believed only in "facts" and was fond of conducting experiments without a guiding hypothesis. But Bernard, with all his esteem for his master whom he regarded as far above the average empiricist, realized that raw facts have no meaning in themselves, that so-called "facts" are often indeed abstractions.[2] He was disposed to see the exemplar of barren empiricism in Sir Francis Bacon, whose importance, he thought, was vastly overrated by historians of science and philosophy. The fertile method in science is that of experimental verification of hypotheses. As he writes in the *Introduction:*

> An anticipated idea of hypothesis is the necessary point of departure of all experimental reasoning. Without that . . . one could only pile up sterile observations. If one experimented without a preconceived idea, one would be acting at random; but on the other hand, if

one *observed* with preconceived ideas, one would make poor observations and run the risk of taking one's own conceptions for reality.[3]

In other words, neither pure speculation nor blind experiment can be of use in scientific work. As observer, the scientist must avoid imposing his ideas on nature; but as experimenter, he cannot proceed in a meaningful way without them.

Now it is through overlooking this dual, or, if you will, this dialectical character of scientific procedure that Félix Ravaisson and Elme Caro, for example, were able, at least to their own satisfaction, to turn Claude Bernard into an idealist, a believer in innate ideas. Caro finds inspiration in Bernard's account of experimental discovery. In scientific research, some hint or insight flashes into the scientist's mind, and may or may not be confirmed by experiment. In his ardent desire for finding arguments in support of his philosophy, Caro manages to forget or to minimize the provisional character and fallibility of such hunches. In a lyrical passage he repaints on the *tabula rasa* of Locke the reminiscences of Platonic idealism:

> I do not know of any more striking tribute to the fertile spontaneity of the mind, and to its creative activity, than this theory of scientific invention, confirmed by the most famous representatives of the experimental school. The mind is therefore capable by a lucky conception of seizing the secrets hidden in the heart of nature, of interpreting by anticipation, before the experiment, the great laws that nature conceals from us under the tangled woof of phenomena! . . . No doubt the experimental school admonishes us to infinite precautions . . . but still it is from within us, from our ideas, from the depths of our mind . . . that every discovery emerges. . . .[4]

Whereas Caro rescues innate ideas by identifying them with Bernard's experimental hypotheses, Ravaisson finds his innate idea in the order of nature, in the determinism of Bernard. He writes in *La Philosophie en France au XIXe siècle:*

> Whereas, according to M. Stuart Mill, we proceed in induction from one assertion about a fact to an assertion about an analogous fact by means of a sheer mech-

anism for which there is no reason we need inquire after; according to M. Claude Bernard, to the contrary, we base ourselves . . . on a principle, an *a priori* axiom, a genuine innate idea . . . the very composition of our intellect, namely, that there is in everything proportion and order, that there is nothing without reason. . . . He says somewhere in terms that one would find in Descartes, Leibniz, Plato . . . that in the experimental method as in everything else, the definitive criterion is reason.[5]

The reproach directed against Mill may indeed be a valid one, in so far as it calls attention to the mechanical character of Mill's associationism. But there is nothing in Bernard's language which supports the idealistic meaning Ravaisson confers on the word "raison." In a similar manner, a younger contemporary of Ravaisson, Jules Lachelier, cites Bernard in an effort to demonstrate that the rational order of nature which makes induction possible is an argument for idealism.[6] There is, however, no warrant in Bernard's text for such an inference. To believe in the intelligibility of the world is not to believe that ideas are the basic reality. Nor is Bernard's critique of Baconian induction, his defense of deductive reasoning, a proof of idealism. Bernard answered all such interpretations in the posthumously published *Cahier rouge:* "The rationalist philosophers who have tried to put everything into the reason which grasps relations have been mistaken. . . ."[7] Ravaisson appears overeager to enlist the physiologist under his own banner. All one can safely conclude is that Bernard was a rationalist, against empiricism. He was a Cartesian in certain aspects of his scientific method. Whether he was a Cartesian in metaphysics is a more complicated question which, whatever the answer, does not validate Ravaisson's opinion.

If Ravaisson sought, on the basis of Bernard's philosophy of scientific method, to make of him an objective idealist, other commentators have tended to underestimate the theoretical contributions of Bernard, and to see in him something very close to a raw empiricist. One of these is Dr. Pierre Mauriac. He is rather unusual among writers on Bernard in that he considers the *Introduction* largely obsolete, and inferior in interest to the *Leçons de pathologie expérimentale*. Going so far as to say that Bernard had a "blind faith in experiment," he reads him a lesson on the naïveté of the scientist who puts too much trust in the facts discovered in the laboratory: "The scientific fact is not the raw fact; it is partly the work of the scientist who selects its conditions and the instruments to measure it. As P. Duhem repeated, the fact and the sciences vary in accordance with the nature of the conditions and the instruments."[8] One can hardly believe that the object of these somewhat patronizing remarks is the same Claude Bernard who set forth that penetrating analysis and critique of empiricism in the very book Dr. Mauriac calls out-of-date. Two pages later, however, Dr. Mauriac hints at his real purpose. It is to attack the "scientism" of which Bernard was the somewhat reluctant but insufficiently resisting accomplice. The opposite and one-sided reactions of Dr. Mauriac and Ravaisson seem in effect to cancel each other out. At the same time, the two extremes serve to indicate the depth and richness of Bernard's thought, which accords both reason and experience their proper place and clarifies their interrelationship.

It is curious that Ravaisson, who was so ready to equate the rationalism of Bernard with idealism, should in another context seek sanction for irrationalism. Living organisms, he opines, are the result of elementary spontaneous movements which cannot be the objects of calculation and reasoning.[9] Bernard's expression, "Life is creation," provided for Ravaisson, Caro, Renouvier, and a long line of successors a support for their opposition to materialism. The various formulations made by Bernard of the relation of life to its physicochemical conditions have permitted divergent constructions. On the one hand he regarded vital phenomena as dependent on the laws of mechanics and chemistry. On the other hand, he put forward the concept of the "creative or directive idea." "That which belongs essentially to the domain of life, and which belongs neither to chemistry, physics, nor anything else, that is the directive *idea* of this vital development."[10] In another work he has the rather cryptic statement "The vital force *directs* phenomena which it does not produce; the physical agents produce phenomena which they do not direct."[11] Is it any wonder that different constructions have been placed on his views, with the idealists Caro, Renouvier, Ravaisson, the vitalist Driesch, and the Thomist Sertillanges opposing the materialists Letourneau, Faure, and Roger? Sheer weight of numbers would seem to turn the balance in favor of idealism, for we could add to its cohorts Paul Janet, A. Ferrand, Émile Boutroux, and Pierre Lamy. Yet their arguments are not conclusive. These arguments, with the exception of the Thomist position of Sertillanges, can all be reduced to one, with individual variations of style and emphasis. Consequently it is not necessary to review them each in detail.[12] We shall concentrate on one, the early and typical discussion of Ravaisson.

The author of the Institute Report on *Philosophy in France in the Nineteenth Century* proceeds in regard to Bernard's "directive idea" in much the same fashion as we have seen him deal with the notion of the *a priori*. Like a football player intercepting the opponents' ball, he seizes the "idée créatrice" and carries it into his desired territory. This tactic may be suitable for a joust of dialectic, not for an attempt to understand what Bernard meant by such expressions. Thus Ravaisson writes: "On his own admission, once life is involved, the consideration of the directive and creative idea becomes indispensable; it is the principal and peculiar object of science."[13] Yet Bernard's research was always oriented toward the physicochemical conditions of vital phenomena, and never was this "directive idea" an object of experiment. As far as his scientific practice was concerned, his position was clear. Had he not called "the metaphysical evolutive force by which we may characterize life, useless in science?" Useless because, existing apart from physical forces, it could exercise no influence upon them.[14] At times he discounts even the directive implication: "Formerly life was regarded as an immaterial principle lodged in organisms to animate and direct the organs . . . such ideas are obsolete. . . ."[15] It is obvious that Bernard's views cannot be reduced to one simple formula.

The phrase "directive or creative idea" was taken by Ravaisson as proof of idealism latent or potential. On the other hand, such expressions were regarded by followers of the Büchner school of materialism like Dr. Charles Letourneau as signs of confusion obscuring a basically materialist stand. With André Lefèvre, translator of Lucretius, Letourneau published in the late 1860's the militant if short-lived materialist organ *La Pensée nouvelle*.[16] He is also remembered for his *Physiologie des Passions* (1868) which Émile Zola read along with Bernard's *Introduction* and Dr. Prosper Lucas' *Traité philosophique et physiologique de l'Hérédité naturelle*.[17] Thus his reaction to Bernard does not lack a certain historical significance. In their confident "scientisme" the editors were glad to set out under the caption "Nos Auxiliaires" an array of quotations from Bernard, alongside extracts from Littré, Sainte-Beuve, Renan, and Taine.[18] Bernard's critique of vitalism was welcomed but his rejection of materialism was disappointing. As Letourneau writes: "There is nothing stranger than Claude Bernard's philosophy; it is a materialistic base, very scientific, very firm, awkwardly bedecked with metaphysical gauze. And what gauze!"[19] There are, to be sure, instances of loose phrasing and traces of confusion in Bernard's writings. This is not surprising in a scientist untrained in philosophy, and influenced by the idealistic tradition of his time; a man, moreover, who was inclined to conform to conventional standards in social and political matters.

Yet he was striving toward a philosophy which neither of the opposing schools of interpretation recognized. This is something above and beyond the fact that, for a thinker who rejected in science both materialism and idealism, his anti-idealistic arguments are more forceful than his antimaterialistic reservations.[20] Unlike the Ravaissons who with their linguistic thaumaturgy try to conjure up the spirit of idealism, Bernard studies the phenomena of life with a cautious natural piety, and hesitates to put too much weight on a mere word. His point of view is not, however, the agnostic or skeptical suspension of judgment which it was characteristic of Renan to emphasize.[21] We find in one of the fragments published by Delhoume a thought eloquent in its simplicity: "Ni ceux qui mettent une âme ni ceux qui mettent une cornue dans le corps vivant n'ont raison. Il faut y mettre ce qu'il y a."[22] ("Neither those who put a soul into the living body nor those who see in it a chemical retort are in the right. We may assume only what is there.") If it were not for a certain carelessness in the construction which might tempt an irreverent reader to give it an incongruous translation, this statement could well serve to express the basic viewpoint of Bernard. Another fragment voices the same suspicion of phrases and formulae, the same respect for nature in its complexity: "My whole philosophy consists, not in holding on tooth and nail to an idea, but in the observation of the rich world of nature." And with the same pride as when in a personal note he called himself the leader of the contemporary movement in physiology, he could add to the statement of his credo just quoted: "That opens up new horizons for me and makes me original."[23] Not vanity, we may remark, but a kind of modest pride justified by an unremitting devotion to his task.

His intent absorption in natural phenomena coupled with his wariness before verbal formulae is nowhere more impressively shown than in the notes for his 1877 lectures at the Muséum. These are the more revealing because, not in final form for presentation, they give us his spontaneous thinking:

> I am going to begin my course with a definition of life. That seems contrary to the scientific spirit. As a matter of fact I begin my course with the definition of life in order to prove that there is no definition, and that we must not, like the philosophers, set up an initial definition that we then regard as an inviolable axiom. . . . Therefore life is not to be defined. But we must have some common basis of understanding.[24]

In a more finished form in the same manuscript notebook he continues: "It is our opinion that these attempts to define life are chimerical, not only because we cannot, but because we need not define it." Yet there is no mysticism involved. Bernard's sheaf of metaphors for life may put one in mind of Renan's rich jewel case of synonyms for God. Thus he may call it various things— torch, candle, journey—or say like Hegel, "La vie c'est la mort." But he is no Pyrrhonist. A science of life can be developed without starting out with a definition. For the aim of physiology is not to define but to master life. There is a striking note of activism or pragmatism in assertions like the following: "Without knowing what life is, I believe we must master it."[25] Almost an echo of Marx's: "Heretofore philosophers have explained the world; now the thing to do is to change it!" In another place Bernard writes: "None of my ideas are part of a system; they are practical ideas."[26] Suggestive of the outlook of John Dewey is the declaration: "Mankind seems to have understood today that its aim is not passive contemplation, but progress and action."[27]

Far from becoming the cornerstone of an idealist's temple as Ravaisson hopes, the concept of the "creative and directive idea" remained for Bernard a theme for speculation rather than an object of research. Reading his notes and published writings, one frequently comes upon such thoughts as the following, variations on the notion of the "creative idea": "There are two forces in physiology: the *legislative* force, metaphysical, directive, creative, and plastic, and the *executive* force which is physical, chemical, and specialized in its modes of action." The "legislative" force is identified with organic growth.[28] But like the absentee God of the eighteenth-century deists, this force no longer intervenes after a species has been created. It has become little more than a figure of speech. In an unpublished note extremely revealing in the words crossed out, this idea is clearly set forth:

> The vitalists are like the Catholics: they *suppose* [crossed out] admit a God or vital force always present, intervening at every moment in vital phenomena. *There is perhaps* [crossed out] one must admit an original force, a God, but the laws having once been established, everything is arranged and the primordial force no longer intervenes.[29]

Finally we may cite more fully a passage in which the author tries to explain what he means by this much-mooted expression:

> In saying that life is the directive idea or the developmental force of the living being, we simply mean the idea in the succession of all the morphological and chemical changes produced by the germ from the beginning to the end of life. Our minds grasp this unity as a conception which compels acceptance, and we explain it as a force. But it would be wrong to believe that this metaphysical force is active in the manner of a physical force. This conception does not leave the intellectual domain to react on the phenomena for the explanation of which the mind had created it.[30]

This clarification was published after the idealistic interpretations of Janet, Caro, and Ravaisson, but it would have been easy for later commentators like Boutroux and Lamy to take it into account, before making the "directive idea" into their main argument for proving the "idealism" of Bernard.[31]

More sophisticated is the attempt of Père Sertillanges to put a Thomist construction on the idea. Is his interpretation more than an ingenious intellectual edifice? Sertillanges tells us that he knew personally Père Didon, the Dominican student and friend of Bernard's last years.[32] Moreover, Sertillanges has studied Bernard's work with great care. His edition of the *Introduction* with its detailed explanatory annotations is sufficient demonstration.[33] Yet his *Philosophie de Claude Bernard* is an adaptation rather than a presentation of Bernard's thought. His identification of the "directive idea" with Aquinas's "substantial form" seems in violation of the spirit of Bernard, his opposition to systems, his skepticism about formulae. Typical of Sertillanges's treatment is the following statement: ". . . he would have said, if he had been better informed on the history of doctrines . . . I am an Aristotelian, in the mode and according to the exact interpretation of Thomism."[34] The plain fact remains that Bernard never did say anything of the kind. All Bernard's references to Scholasticism are derogatory.[35] Sertillanges's book is a fascinating example of a subtle and learned Thomist professor correcting the defective dissertation of a brilliant but misinformed pupil. In the end we have left before us not the work of the pupil, who in this case happens to be Claude Bernard, but a trimmed and polished model assignment for a Dominican seminary.

Up to now the question of "First Causes" and of Bernard's conception of determinism has been with us implicitly, but for the sake of clarity and emphasis it has not been raised explicitly. On this matter, unlike the case of the "directive idea," it is the materialistic critics who are satisfied, whereas the idealists are embarrassed. From Paul Janet and Ravaisson through Brunetière down to Lamy and Dr. Mauriac, the problem has disturbed the advocates of free will. Of these reactions those of Brunetière and Lamy can be taken as examples. Brunetière cannot conceive how Bernard could find determinism consistent with moral liberty. "Isn't there a contradiction there? If universal determinism while conditioning moral freedom still allows it to exist, does not the mere fact of its existence, once recognized, remove it from under the law of a more ultimate determinism?"[36] Brunetière believes that moral freedom introduces into historical or critical problems a disturbing element of indeterminacy which will prevent moral sciences from ever falling under the jurisdiction of physical and chemical forces.

Obviously the full meaning of Bernard's view is not encompassed by Brunetière's blunt reaction. A more devious approach is that of Lamy, who also welcomes the admission of free will, and also sees in it a factor of indeterminacy. On other grounds he takes pains to minimize the bearing of Bernard's determinism. It is evident that the main target of Lamy's book is Faure's treatment of Bernard as a "matérialiste impénitent." Lamy's analysis turns on a subtle distinction which he calls fundamental between "conditions of manifestation" which are physical and "causes of existence" which transcend the physical. "Everything is *manifested* in life through the intervention of physical and chemical conditions."[37] Lamy takes comfort from this partly verbal distinction, which would mean that vital phenomena are conditioned but not caused by physical and chemical factors. It is true that Bernard's phrasing sometimes appears to justify this interpretation. But his own distinction between causes and conditions actually relegated first causes to a metaphysical limbo, and it was a distinction which made no difference so far as his belief in determinism was concerned.

Among the defenders of Bernard's determinism, this notion of first cause is regarded as a vestige of outmoded thought. Thus Henri Roger writes: "Claude Bernard does not succeed in freeing himself completely from the old notion of first causes." For Roger, Bernard is a victim of the split between reason and feeling: "While feeling attached him to idealistic conceptions, reason inclined him to espouse materialism, or more exactly, since the word 'materialism' is devoid of meaning, physicochemical dynamism."[38] No doubt Roger means that the word "materialism" has lost its meaning as a result of the reduction of matter to energy formulae. As a scientific rationalist he harbors none of the doubts or reservations he discovers in Bernard. To the latter's agnosticism he rejoins decisively: "Let us wait confidently, for there are no insoluble problems, but only badly posed questions." He indorses Bernard's affirmation: "Physiological determinism allows of no restriction. . . . Mental phenomena, to manifest themselves, need material conditions that are exactly determined . . . not arbitrarily or capriciously by a lawless spontaneity." But in Roger's opinion, Bernard does not remain consistent with this clear-cut determinism: "After such clear-cut statements, Claude Bernard recoils; like Leibniz he is terrified by the spectacle of fatalism."[39] Roger charges him with a timid compromise between a forthright determinism and a conventional idealism. Yet there may be a valid point involved in Bernard's belief in a determinism that, far from destroying moral freedom, would be in fact a necessary basis for it. As he expressed it: "We are of necessity free."[40]

The phrase is suggestive of the existentialist "We are condemned to be free." Bernard, of course, is no existentialist. His conception seems to deserve neither Roger's censure nor Lamy's congratulations. The freedom of choice which he posits within set conditions contradicts fatalism but falls into place naturally in a determinist scheme. Free will is possible on a deterministic basis, but is a will-of-the-wisp if indeterminism is true. Bernard's insistence upon free will within determinism is not therefore a retreat, as, from their opposing camps, Roger and Lamy assure us, but simply an attempt at a clarification of the issues. Freedom of choice is not for Bernard, as it seems to be for Lamy and Brunetière, an exception to natural law, a negation of determinism. Nor is it a flaw in the cosmos, as Roger appears to regard it. It is nothing metaphysical. It is a fact of nature, occurring under certain conditions, absent under other conditions.

We have sought to define the thought of Claude Bernard on three major topics by comparing the divergent and sometimes diametrically opposite interpretations. On the question of scientific method we find him to be a rationalist who stops short of idealism, a naturalist who goes beyond empiricism, a nominalist suspicious of formulae, a skeptic in regard to systems, but a confident believer in theory, in reason, and in the intelligibility of natural phenomena. On the question of the nature of life we find him steadfast in his belief that physiology becomes scientific when vital phenomena are accounted for in terms of physical and chemical conditions. He is opposed to vitalism because it pretends to explain life in the light of some immaterial force. His *idée directrice* is perhaps an unfortunate choice of words, but it is justified in so far as it emphasizes the distinctive character of vital processes. While entirely rooted in physicochemical conditions, life represents a higher level of organization, requiring an explanation in terms of this higher level. Finally, on the question of determinism we see in him a consistent determinist whose notion of free will makes sense within the context of objective determinism. His concept has no real affinity with that element of indeterminacy or contingency which Brunetière and Lamy mistakenly hailed, and which Boutroux for his part sought to introduce into the texture of natural law.[41]

CHAPTER Five

Claude Bernard and Modern Thought: Influences and Implications

IN THEIR RESPONSES to Bernard's exposition of scientific method, determinism, and the physical basis of life, philosophers like Caro and Paul Janet were more interested in reconciling it with traditional idealism than in weighing it as a contribution to knowledge. In other words, they sought rather to relate it to the past than to ponder its meaning for the future. They all tried to enlist him in their campaigns against materialism, or against the positivism of Comte. On the other hand, materialists like Letourneau aimed at using him against their idealist adversaries. Thus both camps tended to obscure rather than to illuminate the novelty and originality of his achievements. Coming a century after, we enjoy an advantage over his contemporaries, even if it is only the advantage of hindsight, as we attempt to measure his long-term significance. Al-

79

though some overlapping is unavoidable, the bearing of his work will here be studied in accordance with the following outline: first, physiology and psychology; second, scientific method; third, philosophy and general ideas. It will not be a story of ever-expanding influence, such as might be told for Copernicus or Newton. It would be unjust to Bernard himself to speak grandiloquently of an "Age of Claude Bernard," or of a "Maître à penser universel," as certain enthusiasts have done. Many of his contributions have merged into the complex web of modern science, yet some of the strands can still be traced.

I Physiology and Psychology

In a preceding chapter we touched on a few typical reactions to Bernard's theories on the relation of physiology to the physical sciences. On the one hand, there were those readers who insisted that Bernard was essentially a materialist whose thought was vitiated by traces of idealism. On the other hand, there were those who saw in phrases like "the creative or directive idea of life" a confession of idealism. We tried to show that Bernard taken as a whole could not be encompassed by either of these contrasting formulae. His idée créatrice was a misleading phrase which was perhaps taken too seriously by the idealists. His main emphasis was on the fact that physiology, while rooted in the physicochemical sciences, occupies a domain of its own which cannot be reduced completely to the laws of the inorganic realm. One of the fairest judgments of Bernard's position is that of W. Riese who states: "The view that life is due to creation as to a causa sui generis can be considered as a vitalistic element which Claude Bernard never gave up in spite of his . . . physicochemical determinism. He therefore is neither a vitalist nor a materialist. Only a critical view of life . . . traces of which are to be found in the work of Claude Bernard, can save us from a permanent wavering between these two dogmatic conceptions."[1] It is the vitalistic element mentioned by Riese which provoked the rejoinder of the physiologist Jacques Loeb, noted for his work on tropisms. This staunch mechanist wrote in his book The Organism as a Whole: "Claude Bernard who in the investigation of the individual life processes, was a strict mechanist, declares that the making of a harmonious organism from the egg cannot be explained on a mechanistic basis but only on the assumption of a 'directive force.' " Loeb cites a number of discoveries which in his view have changed the picture since the time of Bernard: "This attitude of Bernard would be incomprehensible but for the fact that, when he made these statements, the phenomena of specificity, the physiology of development and regeneration, the Mendelian laws of heredity, the animal tropisms and their bearing on the theory of adaptation were unknown."[2] A similar rebuttal based on progress in physiology subsequent to Bernard is made by Jean-Louis Faure. If only Bernard had known of Leduc's research on *karyokinesis,* on ink blots paralleling cellular movements![3] Bernard had combatted the vitalism of Bichat, and now seemed to have compromised with its avatar. This image of Bernard as virtually a neo-vitalist was quite common in writings appearing in the earlier decades of the present century.[4] It seemed to many that Bernard was a figure who could safely be consigned to a past epoch of scientific history, honored but unsung.

It might surprise a writer like Félix Le Dantec, who was one of those who felt that Bernard had had his day, to discover how frequently he is mentioned in connection with some of the most recent advances in science. It was inevitable that some part of his work should come to seem obsolete with the further progress of the physiology he helped to promote. But there is one basic insight we owe to Bernard which has continued to exert a seminal influence on contemporary science. It is the concept of the *milieu intérieur.* Yet although he stated it quite early and repeatedly, its full potentialities were not generally realized until decades after his death. The basic significance is suggested by the words of the historian of physiology John F. Fulton: "One can again approach the human body as a single functional entity. The first great step toward this goal was taken in 1878 by Claude Bernard who enunciated the conception. . . ."[5] The lateness of the date given by Fulton is explained by the fact that he fails to refer to any writings earlier than *Les Phénomènes de la vie,* published in 1878. Extracting some passages from this work for his *Selected Readings in the History of Physiology,* Fulton writes: "Perhaps greater than all [his other discoveries] was his teaching concerning the internal environment of the organism, Bernard's last published work, and the outcome of a life of profound thought. Little appreciated at the time, this far-reaching conception has now come into its own, and . . . it will undoubtedly exert a great influence on the physiology of the future."[6] Bernard's first English biographer, Sir Michael Foster, makes only a bare mention of it in 1899.[7] The later biographer J. M. D. Olmsted observes that the concept made little impression until the twentieth century, although he does mention that Bernard's pupil Dastre recognized its importance.[8] Olmsted could have included the Belgian zoologist Léon Fredericq and Bernard's follower Charles Richet, both of whom are cited by Walter B. Cannon.[9] Only one of these references goes as far back as 1885.

Yet certain of Bernard's contemporaries were quite aware of the concept. They include such well-known men as William James, George Henry Lewes, and Charles Renouvier. The *North American Review* in 1868 published an article by James on Bernard's *Rapport sur le progrès et la marche de la physiologie générale en France.* It is striking that one of the subjects which most impressed the budding American philosopher was precisely the *internal medium.* "Man is an aquatic animal;" he writes, "that is his *immediate* life, which is only the life of his cells, can only subsist in a watery medium." James continues: "It is no small service of M. Bernard's that he has put the expression *internal medium* into circulation." It is perhaps significant that the young medical student, who was to abandon physiology for psychology and then for philosophy, was not too sanguine about the prospects of that science: "The brilliant accomplishments M. Bernard hopes for are in the very dimmest future. . . . We are still ignorant of the laws of cell nutrition."[10] In the remainder of the article James turns with approval to a lecture by Dr. Oliver Wendell Holmes in which the Autocrat of the Breakfast-Table attacks what he regards as overemphasis of science in medical education. Thus James seems to indorse an attitude which goes exactly contrary to Bernard's general position on the importance of physiology for medicine. And he says no more about the specific concept of the inner medium.

A more systematic application is made by the English positivist, G. H. Lewes, in his *Problems of Life and Mind*. The companion of the novelist George Eliot, the friend of Mill, Darwin, and Spencer, may have helped to counteract the stereotype of the heartless vivisectionist which the name of Claude Bernard evoked in the minds of many Victorians.[11] Lewes's book contains many references to him, in particular to the work on the nervous system.[12] In Lewes's discussion of the physical basis of mind, he distinguishes between the External or Cosmical Medium, and the Internal or Physiological Medium, which is the plasma in which the tissues are bathed. He discusses along with the plasma, the temperature, and the electrical conditions of the medium, thus anticipating with Bernard the research of Cannon and Barcroft. But Lewes's remarks on the internal medium are those of a reader and not an experimental scientist. His attempt to fit it into the theory of evolution is noteworthy: he uses it to dispute an objection of Darwin's adversary Agassiz which concerned the alleged absence of direct influence on the organism exerted by external conditions. Lewes felt that the inner medium helps to explain the great variety of biological forms found in the same external conditions, whereas Agassiz had considered this diversity to be an argument against Darwinism.[13] The death of Lewes soon after the writing of this book put an end to the possibility that he might have given greater currency to the concept of the Inner Medium.

Quite different from Lewes's positivist approach is the reaction of Charles Renouvier, the neo-criticist so admired by William James. It is curious that this philosopher takes a sort of tender-minded consolation from the notion, finding in the inner environment a sanctum for the mystery of life, and a support for indeterminism against determinism: "The physiologist envisages the 'inner' milieu as the one in which we live, rather than in the great milieu, the external world with which we have no direct contact."[14] Thus one of the earlier allusions to the idea is concerned much more with a dubious metaphysical implication than with its physiological significance.

Illustrative of the greater interest taken in the concept after the turn of the century is the rather extensive research enterprise of René Quinton. He continues the work of Léon Fredericq, cited above, on the influence of the saltiness of ocean water on the blood of crustaceans.[15] In his book entitled *L'Eau de mer milieu organique,* he is obviously indebted to Bernard for his point of departure. Quinton's thesis is his law of "constance marine," namely, that the blood retains the general composition of sea water which was the original vital medium. Vertebrates have simply developed further a condition still found in the sponges and coral polyps in which sea water is in direct contact with the cells. The work is well buttressed with tables of the chemical constituents of salt and fresh water as well as of various biological organisms. One is somewhat taken aback by the author's grudging reference to Bernard: "Here we renounce the expression of *milieu intérieur,* offered by Claude Bernard, as being inadequate, first, to designate a medium which is *par excellence* external to the cell, the only element considered in this book, and second, as inapplicable to a portion of the animal kingdom."[16] Quinton has philosophical ambitions. Reminding us of Bergson's *élan vital,* he conceives of life in evolution as a power resisting its environment and maintaining its primordial conditions. Thus he imposes on the data collected a finalist interpretation, with a distinct anti-Darwinian twist. It is partly because of this metabiological tendency that Quinton became for a moment a bright star in the scientific heaven for a whole group of literary men early in the century. Charles Maurras, Maurice Barrès, and Paul Bourget saw in him a scientist bringing prestige to their nationalist cause. Less influenced by political motives was the admiration of Remy de Gourmont, Jules de Gaultier, and Jean Weber, but even they could not make Quinton's doctrine much more than a *curiosum,* a byway in the history of biology.[17]

It is with the researches of J. S. Haldane and Lawrence J. Henderson that Bernard's teaching really began to show its suggestive value. Henderson's treatise on *Blood* is cited by Fulton as an example of its influence.[18] Henderson himself has more than once acknowledged the impact of Bernard's ideas. In his valuable introduction to H. C. Greene's translation of the *Introduction to the Study of Experimental Medicine,* Henderson suggests a reason for the tardy recognition of the concept: "The theory of the *internal environment* . . . we owe almost entirely to Claude Bernard himself. . . . Today with the aid of a physical chemistry unknown to the contemporaries of Claude Bernard, it is fulfilling the promise which he alone could clearly see."[19] J. S. Haldane's study of *Respiration* was another sign of the times.[20] But neither Haldane nor Henderson was content with the verifiable implications of the concept. The inner medium involves the whole question of the coordination of physiological processes. This becomes their springboard into speculations on the philosophy of the organism. The coordination or organization of these processes was regarded by Haldane and Henderson as transcending the plane of physicochemical explanation. In their metaphysical writings, they gave a more modern turn to the antimechanistic arguments we have met in Janet and Caro. Henderson's book *The Order of Nature* finds in Bernard implications which justify the finalism of Lachelier, while Haldane's *The Sciences and Philosophy* argues for a unitary or organismic philosophy rejecting both mechanism and the old-fashioned vitalism combatted by Bernard. Both detect clear indications of organicism in Bernard, but deplore the unclarity of thought which, in their view, permitted him to cling to the mechanistic position.[21]

Subsequent applications of Bernard's teaching are untroubled by such metaphysical tendencies. We recall that it was through his research on glycogenesis that Bernard was enabled to make his discovery of the constancy of the inner medium. His realization of the full import of this truth came gradually. At first he considered the blood plasma to be the only milieu, then he added the lymph to the system, and only later spoke of the "totality of the circulating fluids." The necessary constants came to include water, oxygen, temperature, and supplies of fats and sugars. Later investigations have added internal secretions to the list. If there is a scientific classic devoted to research on the constancy of the inner matrix, it is certainly *The Wisdom of the Body* by Walter B. Cannon. In his preface to the French translation, Cannon pronounced a ringing eulogy of Bernard: "The central idea of this book, 'the stability of the inner medium of the organism in higher vertebrates,' is directly inspired by the precise views and deep understanding of the eminent French physiologist Claude Bernard. This book can even be considered a tribute to his memory."[22] In his chapter on the "fluid matrix," Cannon notes Bernard's priority in specifying the role of the inner environment in the establishment and maintenance of steady states in the body. "It was a signal contribution," writes Cannon, "to our understanding of physiology that Bernard made when he recognized that the blood and the interstitial lymph provide appropriate and favorable surroundings for the living cells of the organism."[23] Cannon gave the name *homeostasis* to these steady states maintained in the body. He felt the need for a specific term to apply to physiological equilibria, which are much more complex than physicochemical equilibria. It would carry us too far even to summarize Cannon's absorbing account of the various factors involved, the constancy of water, salt, sugar, protein, fats in the blood, oxygen supply, acid-alkaline neutrality, and body temperature, as well as the role of the sympathetic nervous system in all this. The attainment of a detailed understanding of this intricate subject required the efforts of scores of investigators. Cannon has incorporated their reports into his book, but his own dominant place is clearly evident. It is a tribute to the scientific insight of Bernard that Cannon should think of this vast research program as having been set into motion by Bernard's statement: "All the vital mechanisms, however varied they may be, have only one object, that of preserving constant the conditions of life in the inner environment." As J. S. Haldane wrote: "No more pregnant sentence was ever framed by a physiologist."[24]

Other outstanding modern physiologists who might be considered descendants of Bernard include Sir Joseph Barcroft and Sir Charles Sherrington in England. The latter noted in his awkward yet effective style: "That life overcomes the obstacles of unfavourable environment by manufacturing a piece of environment suited to itself and carrying it about with it, Claude Bernard was the first to detect."[25] The imprint of the French scientist is conspicuous in Barcroft's *Features in the Architecture of Physiological Function*. The first three chapters bear the epigraph: *"La Fixité du Milieu Intérieur est la Condition de la Vie Libre"* (Claude Bernard).

Haldane, Henderson, and Cannon had increased our understanding of the mechanisms which secure the constancy of the internal medium and demonstrated the exactness with which these mechanisms operate. Thus the first part of Bernard's principle, the subject of his clause, appears to have been pretty adequately established. But what about the predicate of his clause? Barcroft undertakes to clarify this second term of Bernard's proposition, which he finds provocatively vague. In the course of his exposition Barcroft demonstrates that it is the higher nervous system, rather than the grosser bodily functions, which is impaired when homeostasis is disturbed. As he lyrically puts it: "To look for a high intellectual development in a *milieu* whose properties have not become stabilized is to seek music amongst the crashings of a rudimentary wireless or ripple-patterns on the surface of the stormy Atlantic."[26] Thus Bernard's vague phrase, "la vie libre," is vindicated by Barcroft, who provides it with a factual content.

Among the constants involved in homeostasis are the internal secretions. Already in 1865 Bernard first called attention to what he termed "sécrétions internes." Although, technically speaking, modern views of the subject do not agree with Bernard's, his initiating genius has been acknowledged by historians. Fielding H. Garrison writes: "The starting-point of the doctrine of internal secretions was Claude Bernard's work on the glycogenic function."[27] The same historian gives a more extended account in his "History of Endocrine Doctrine." Garrison shows how Bernard's work, along with that of Thomas Addison on the suprarenal glands, led to the birth of a new science—endocrinology. The importance for psychology of this new science is signalized by G. Dumas, who cites the analysis of E. Gley. Gley is even more emphatic than Garrison in stressing the pioneering role played by Bernard.[28] Bernard's successor in the Collège de France, the ubiquitous Brown-Séquard, inaugurated the investigation of hormones with his somewhat notorious research on the male hormone. Eventually the whole broad domain of endocrinology was to be opened up.

A striking fact is the frequency with which the name of Bernard is invoked by modern physiologists, striking because it follows a period of several decades when his fame seemed to have been definitely embalmed in the history of science. Strands now lead back to Bernard from several recently founded sciences. Let us take up one of these strands again. This is the concept of self-regulation of body organs. Elie de Cyon noted that Bernard had sensed its bearing as early as 1868 in his report on the nerves regulating the action of the heart discovered by Cyon. The latter compared this effect to that of a safety valve.[29] The well-known worker on human and electronic brains, W. Grey Walter, has recently acknowledged the significance for him of Barcroft's expansion of Bernard's dictum on the constancy of the inner environment. The principle is like a node linking the fields of physiology and the new science of cybernetics. Norbert Wiener picks up the strand when he writes: "Walter Cannon, going back to Claude Bernard, emphasized that the health and even the very existence of the body depends on what are called homeostatic processes. . . . the apparent equilibrium of life is an active equilibrium, in which each deviation from the norm brings on a reaction in the opposite direction, which is of the nature of what we call negative feedback."[30] Wiener closes one chapter of his book *Cybernetics* with an arresting description of the principle: "Our inner economy must contain an assembly of thermostats, automatic hydrogen-ion concentration controls, governors and the like, which would be adequate for a great chemical plant."[31] One of Wiener's associates has been the cardiologist Arturo Rosenblueth, himself a former co-worker of Cannon. Part of the story of the collaboration of Wiener and Rosenblueth is retold in Pierre de Latil's *La Pensée artificielle,* in which Bernard's doctrine is declared to be one of the *idées-mères* of cybernetics.[32]

A further offshoot of Cannon's homeostasis is the research of Hans Selye on stress. This is the term chosen by Selye to designate the type of situation in which the organism finds itself when its homeostatic balance is threatened by hostile agencies.

The investigation of so-called stress has expanded enormously in recent years. It includes what H. Laborit has termed "organic reaction to aggression and shock." Related to it is René Leriche's work on post-surgical disorders. Selye has been interested in finding in organisms "a general non-specific reaction pattern." Stress is defined as the state which manifests itself by the G.A.S., or general adaptation syndrome, which comprises such reactions as adrenal stimulation, shrinkage of lymphatic organs, gastrointestinal ulcers, loss of body-weight, alteration of the chemical constitution.[33] And we observe again that the leaders in this field acknowledge their indebtedness to Bernard.[34] Inspired by Bernard and Cannon, Selye saw that "disease is not just suffering, but a fight to maintain the homeostatic balance of our tissues, despite damage." It was in this light that he began his search for certain measures, which would be nonspecific, and might serve in the cure of almost any disease.[35]

These striking discoveries of Cannon, Barcroft, Wiener, and Selye are the signs of a far-reaching change of perspective in physiological science. In his *Progress in Medicine* (1940), Dr. Iago Galdston traces this change from the post-Pasteurian period when disease was regarded as almost entirely the effect of germs. As Galdston puts it: "The reign of the microbes has been severely challenged during the last twenty-five years. Experience and new knowledge have brought to light the important role played by nutrition, the glands of internal secretion, and mental and emotional factors in the maintenance of health and in the origin of disease." Galdston cites the famous physician Sir William Osler's conception of "seed and soil" in the development of disease. And he does not fail to recognize the slow-acting influence of Claude Bernard in this change of perspective. The surgeon Leriche remarks that "we are coming back to Bernard," while modifying his doctrine that pathology is but an extension of physiology.[36] Hans Selye, too, has taken occasion to correct the undue dominance of bacteriology over physiology. In writings and lectures Selye has presented an interesting sidelight on the popularly accepted comparison which sets Pasteur above Bernard. He recalls the debates between the two scientists about the relative importance in disease of the microbe and the condition of the body. Pasteur insisted on the importance of the germ, while Bernard stressed the equilibrium of the organism. Selye quotes the admission Pasteur made on his deathbed to Professor Rénon: "Bernard avait raison. Le germe n'est rien, c'est le terrain qui est tout."[37] ("Bernard was right. The germ is nothing, the medium is everything.") It is to be noted that Osler's "seed and soil" analogy is but the translation of the terms used by Pasteur. In his chapter on tuberculosis, Osler remarked on the ubiquity of the bacillus which could cause the infection only if the condition of the "soil," the body, made the subject vulnerable.[38]

In view of the present state of physiological science, and the vindication of Bernard which has come about, it is interesting to turn back the pages of history to Pasteur's epic struggles to establish the germ theory of disease. Historical justice requires that both sides of this question be placed in correct perspective. It is certainly true that Bernard underestimated the part played in infection by these microorganisms. He was even inclined upon occasion to scoff at the microbiologists. Thus in a letter to Mme Raffalovich he could write: "Today the experimental spirit is being impoverished and frittered away with nonsense about the infinitely little which has no meaning. That is what is commonly called: 'Chercher la petite bête.' "[39]* Commenting on Bernard's coolness toward the germ theory, Dr. Mauriac is led to suggest that were it not for his deterministic bias, he might have discovered the world of the microbes.[40] Long before Dr. Mauriac, the now-famous American philosopher Charles Peirce, in some notes for a projected history of science, had charged Bernard with a different bias: that of nominalism. Peirce goes so far as to accuse him of responsibility for the opposition encountered by Pasteur: "The medical world was dominated by Claude Bernard's dictum that disease is not an entity but merely a sum of symptoms. This was pure metaphysics which merely barricaded inquiry in that direction. But that was a generation which attached great value to nominalistic metaphysics." According to Peirce, the medical men, dominated by the metaphysics of Claude Bernard, raised all sorts of sophistical objections to Pas-

---

*The French phrase involves a pun on the idiomatic meaning which is "to be overcritical" and the literal use: "to look for the little bug."

teur's efforts to extend the germ theory to various diseases.[41] Peirce cites as evidence of Bernard's "bias" a statement from the *Leçons de pathologie expérimentale*. Bernard does describe disease as consisting, not of "a single symptom, but of a series of symptoms united among themselves by relations of cause and effect."[42] This does not read like a denial of disease as an entity. And what has metaphysics to do with it? It is necessary to invoke neither a nominalistic nor a deterministic bias to explain Bernard's tendency to seek explanations for disease mainly or entirely in the changes in bodily tissues and fluids. Furthermore, Pasteur himself does not seem to have regarded Bernard in the light in which Peirce sees him. Pasteur's published writings and correspondence, as long as Bernard lived, evinced only cordial feelings toward him, as a teacher, sponsor, collaborator, and friend.[43] And the shock Pasteur manifested on Berthelot's publication of Bernard's posthumous notes on fermentation proves how far he was from even dreaming of Bernard as an adversary.

The vicissitudes in the evolution of ideas are well illustrated in the subsequent period called the Reign of the Post-Pasteurians. Peirce saw Bernard in the role of one impeding scientific progress. But one turn of the wheel and the positions are certainly reversed. Let us read what one of Bernard's students, Elie de Cyon, had to say half a century ago on the relations between physiology, bacteriology, and pathology. Reviewing the great advances in bacteriology led by Pasteur, Koch, and Lister, one finds it easy to understand the exaggerated hopes reposed in the science by those disciples who lacked a sufficient knowledge of physiology. The illusion that bacteriology could, alone and unaided, provide a complete basis for medicine had come to prevail in the very homeland of Claude Bernard! Cyon deplores the low state of physiology in France, in regard to university chairs, laboratories, and journals. "Is it surprising, if in France bacteriology has easily brought about an almost complete break between physicians and physiology!" Men ignorant of physiology think themselves capable of easily discovering new bacilli and even inventing serums! The human body is for them only a battlefield for the exploits of microbes and leucocytes, locked in mortal combat. Cyon closes with an appeal for renewal of physiological research in the spirit of Claude Bernard.[44] If he was a voice crying in the wilderness in 1905, Cyon might well believe today that his prayers had been answered.

Jean Rostand and Dr. Mauriac have pointed out a number of insights recorded by Bernard in the posthumous notebooks which today seem clairvoyant when compared to recent discoveries. Of these, we shall take time to mention only two examples. One is the suggestion of artificial perfusion of organs detached from the body along the lines of Bernard's lavation of the liver.[45] This hint was carried out in the spectacular achievements of Dr. Alexis Carrel and Charles Lindbergh in maintaining life in a separated chicken heart.[46] Another prophetic suggestion involved the effect of position on the development of the cell. Bernard asked why one cell becomes an ovum, another develops into muscle fiber: "Is it because this cell has in it a specific developmental virtuality, or entelechy; or is it the fact that it grows *in one place* that makes it take a special form? I am a strong believer in the influence of position."[47] This idea is now demonstrated by the investigation of embryologists like Hans Spemann.[48] It is of particular interest because it shows Bernard staking out a line of thought which was to invalidate some of his own pronouncements so eagerly welcomed by neo-vitalists and teleologists. We have in mind the phrases on the *quid proprium,* the creative and directive idea of life.

The bearing of physiology for the science of psychology justifies us in opening a parenthesis here on Bernard's significance for this area of knowledge. Dr. Delhoume writes that one looks in vain for the name of Bernard in modern treatises on psychology.[49] It is true that the references to him are few and far between, if not lacking, whether one takes up William James's *Principles of Psychology,* the publications of Wilhelm Wundt, or the writings of more recent psychologists. Yet it is possible to make a case for him in the borderland where physiology and psychology adjoin each other. Mention has already been made of Lewes's reading of Bernard, and his adoption of the concept of the Internal Medium, in his book on problems of body and mind. Quite in line with Lewes's approach are the remarks of Henry Maudsley in 1884:

It is impossible for any one who has not made a diligent study of the physiology of the body to appreciate the many and various influences which continually work upon the mind. . . . He apprehends only that which is within the light of consciousness, whereas there are outside it, below its threshold, insensible, a complex composition of intricate forces that is known only or mainly in the result. It is probable . . . that the light-bearing experiments and discoveries of Claude Bernard reflecting the functions of the sympathetic system of nerves and the intimate phenomena of life, might yield him more insight into that matter than all the disquisitions can ever do.[50]

As a critic of the psychology of John Stuart Mill and of the one-sided dependence on the introspective method, it was natural for Maudsley to express such an attitude. The roots of modern psychology lie, of course, largely in physiological soil. Moreover, experimental psychology has utilized the same canons which Bernard had applied in his field. But Bernard was only one physiologist among many others, and his domination of French physiology did not extend with equal force into the land of Helmholtz, Ebbinghaus, and Wundt. Edwin G. Boring describes him as less important for the history of experimental psychology than three earlier physiologists, Bell, Magendie, and Johannes Müller. It is their contribution to neurology which Boring has in mind, and in this respect Bernard's work, being a development of theirs, was less fundamental. Boring does not mention the concept of the internal environment.[51] On the other hand, certain American psychologists have given it a place in the foundations of the theory of personality.[52]

One might expect Bernard's imprint upon French psychology to be more marked than upon British or German. Taine's work *De l'Intelligence* (1870) is less beholden to Bernard in its psychological part than in its treatment of the conception of scientific determinism. More pertinent is the case of Théodule Ribot, whose programmatic statement of the objective of experimental psychology parallels Bernard's approach to physiology: "A purely experimental psychology will have for its object only phenomena, their laws and their immediate causes."[53] The most noteworthy of his allusions to Bernard are to be found in his *Psychologie des sentiments.* Here he extends into psychology the view expounded by Bernard, and previously suggested by Broussais and Comte, that there exists no basic difference between pathological and physiological phenomena. The German philosopher Nietzsche described it, citing Bernard, as a difference only of degree. Disproportion and lack of harmony in normal phenomena constitute disease.[54] The normal state is a conception of the mind, a typical ideal form. As Ribot puts it: "If this is the case with regard to bodily health, how much more so with regard to mental."[55] In another passage, Ribot calls attention to one of Bernard's ventures into psychological territory. In a study on the heart, Bernard had undertaken to show that the popular expressions regarding this organ are not mere metaphors but the result of accurate observation, and that they can be translated into physiological language. This line of thought was continued by his student Cyon. Ribot summarizes their work, but does not subject it to the critical analysis which one feels these suggestive but partial findings would require.[56] These different comments by Ribot on Bernard are enough when taken in conjunction with those of G. Dumas cited above, to indicate that Bernard has not been entirely overlooked by French psychologists, despite the disappointment expressed by Dr. Delhoume. Yet something of this disappointment remains. Needless to say, if we take up other eminent French psychologists, whether Binet, Charcot, or Pierre Janet, we must acknowledge that their areas of study were beyond the radius of significant Bernardian influence.

For any decisive influence, one naturally inquires among those workers in psychology who had moved into this province after a previous stage passed in the domain of physiology. We have already remarked on how fleeting this impact was on the erstwhile physiologist William James. A similar inference can be made for the one-time neurologist Sigmund Freud. In contrast to James and Freud, the role of Bernard in the development of the Russian Ivan P. Pavlov must be regarded as of paramount importance. Biographers of Pavlov record the fact that he was a student of Cyon and Sechenov who both had worked in Bernard's laboratory. One listener at Pavlov's lectures in 1911 recalls the "tremendous physiological drama that he unfolded before our eyes, a great historical chronicle of which the authors were Claude Bernard, . . . Cyon, Brown-Séquard, Sechenov . . . ."[57] It is interesting that Pavlov began his researches in an area which Bernard had made his own: the study of digestion. And it was during these investigations that Pavlov more or less accidentally came upon the observations leading to his discovery of the conditioned reflexes. Furthermore, Pavlov persisted in calling himself a physiologist, long after this discovery had inspired the movement in psychology exemplified by the behaviorism of John B. Watson.

Like Bernard, Pavlov was a consummate technician, and he was able to make his first contribution to the study of digestive glands by means of a perfected form of Bernard's so-called "permanent pancreatic fistula."[58] In a broader sense, Bernard's philosophy of experimental medicine was continued by Pavlov, who proclaimed early in his career in almost Bernardian terms: "Only by passing through the fire of experiment will medicine as a whole become what it should be, namely, a conscious, and hence, always purposefully acting science."[59] Moreover, he restated emphatically Bernard's teaching which denied the existence of a sharp line dividing pathology and physiology.[60] Pavlov differed with Bernard, of course, on specific points. One example is the inhibition of salivary secretion.[61]

Most impressive of all is the fact that Bernard's theory of the inner environment became a cornerstone of Pavlov's system, as the biographer Babkin recognized. Babkin associates Pavlov with the movement of "synthetic" or "integral" physiology in which he includes J. S. Haldane, Sherrington, and Cannon, all having their point of departure in Bernard's principle. In his later years Pavlov formulated his conception of the organism as an "unstable labile system" which is very close to Cannon's doctrine of "homeostasis."[62] How fundamental the "inner environment" is for Pavlov can be seen in the fact that a recent book on Pavlov makes him the originator of the concept without so much as mentioning Claude Bernard.[63] Pavlov's investigation of the cerebral cortex throws light on the function of this organ as a sort of governor "maintaining a dynamic equilibrium between the internal and external environments."[64] Thus Pavlov's researches which bring to fruition Bernard's study on the functions of the brain appear to converge with the brain physiology of Barcroft, discussed above. The link enables us to close at this point our parenthesis on psychology, although we have never been very far from the physiological domain.

In concluding this section of our review, we are moved to wonder again how the concept of the inner medium which has proved so fruitful since 1900 could have remained virtually barren for over a quarter of a century. Why were James, Renouvier, and Lewes almost alone in noticing it? Moreover, one looks for it in vain in James's better-known writings, while for Renouvier it was only a postscript. Contrast this almost complete silence with the endless disquisitions on the *idée directrice* and the *quid proprium* of life which were put into print by the Paul Janets and the Elme-Marie Caros. There was a spate of commentaries down well-worn channels of thought, but hardly a word on an idea which now appears as one of the keys to modern science. The fortunes of the concept provide one more instance of a not infrequent phenomenon of history: an idea is enunciated in advance of its time and must await a change in climate before it can be fully appreciated. Thus the Copernican theory made hardly a ripple for several decades after 1543. In accounting for the delay in exploiting Bernard's concept, Henderson refers to the backwardness of physical chemistry in Bernard's time. A somewhat different reason is given by Shryock, who observes that later advances in biochemistry have enabled investigators to see the possibilities in this line of approach.[65] Still another factor undoubtedly was the dominance of bacteriology in the last quarter of the century, a dominance which, as Cyon deplored, tended to put physiology into the shade. The testimony quoted from Osler, Galdston, and Selye explains, if it does not completely justify, the somewhat biased animadversions of Cyon against the Post-Pasteurians. The vindication of Bernard which we can read in the work of the Haldanes, Cannons, and Pavlovs does not cast the microbe hunters into outer darkness. The once divergent lines of march of bacteriology and physiology are now converging in a biology more complex than either Bernard or Pasteur could have clearly realized. A Hegelian should enjoy discussing this evolution of ideas in terms of his thesis, antithesis, and synthesis.

II Scientific Method

The importance of Bernard's role in the philosophy of science was underlined by Henri Bergson. For the philosopher of creative evolution, Bernard's great contribution lay in his constant endeavor to show how fact and idea must work together in experimental research.[66] Pasteur, too, had extolled the *Introduction to Experimental Medicine* as the clearest, deepest, and most complete exposition of the principles of the art of experiment.[67] But his present rank in the company of philosophers of science is ambiguous. For many writers on the subject nowadays he might never have existed. Of the comments that have been made, some are grudging, if not supercilious. One writer, irked by his attitude toward the Scholastics, calls him "un piètre logicien." Two others, while allowing that a physician might profit from reading him, brush him aside as offering no help to up-to-date logicians.[68] Nevertheless, despite the relative obsolescence into which his work has fallen, it can be demonstrated that his teachings belong in the main stream of modern philosophy of science, and furthermore, that they continue to offer seminal suggestions for contemporary thought. A few authors do use his name to conjure with, and sometimes to good effect. It must, of course, be admitted at the outset that he had little to contribute to the field of logic strictly so-called, and nothing at all in such areas as symbolic logic, that rigorous and subtle discipline which has grown up since his lifetime.

His significance lies elsewhere—in the domain which John Dewey named "experimental logic." Reading various modern treatises on the logic of science, one is irresistibly reminded of Bernard's defense of hypothesis and of his critique of induction. In the outline given in the first chapter, we cited his argument against the sharp division once made between deduction and induction. His pages provide a point of departure for André Lalande, who formulates the relationship as follows: "The contrast [between induction and deduction] is only partial: we pass from one to the other as our knowledge develops: chains of deductive ideas are incorporated more and more into the conduct of experiment and experimental reasoning."[69] Like Lalande, Louis Rougier and Émile Meyerson have paid tribute to Bernard's clarification of this relation between the two processes.[70] But the author of *The Logical Problem of Induction*, G. H. Von Wright, dismisses Bernard as an example of the French psychologizing tendency. Unlike the English with their concern for establishing the logical validity of induction, the French have been mainly interested in how inductions originate from observation.[71] It is of course precisely this process of experimental discovery which Bernard illuminates in his *Introduction*. In a posthumous fragment, he touched on this very point: "I do not seek like the philosophers simply to establish the knowledge acquired, but to learn how it is acquired, and how one can acquire new knowledge. In short I concern myself with scientific invention or discovery which has been neglected by the philosophers and even by Mill."[72] It is in this experimental setting that we must place his defense of hypothesis.

His position in this regard is the same as that which we have defined for his philosophy in general: between the extremes of disembodied rationalism and raw empiricism. In one of his notebooks, he once expressed, perhaps unguardedly, his negative attitude toward pure logic: "Logic, at bottom, is a blind instrument which leads to absurdity as easily as to truth, if one has not had sensitivity to start with. Logic only serves to develop, to transform a *sentiment,* a way of doing. . . ."[73] But pure experience is also not enough. Newton's claim "Hypotheses non fingo" had been taken out of context by some Baconians. Bernard's understanding of Newton was quite different. He saw in Newton an ally against the Scholastics: "Caveant physicos à metaphysica." ("Let physicists beware of metaphysics.") In Bernard's judgment, Newton did in fact posit hypotheses. Bodies fall, the moon revolves, *as if* there were attraction toward the center of the earth: *quasi esset attractio.* But the force of attraction does not exist; it is only a word used to shorten discussion.[74] Hypothesis retains a provisional character, yet it is indispensable to science. Bernard was of course not the first to insist on its function, for this had been clearly treated by Whewell. And Comte had framed a rationale for the employment of hypotheses which accepts them as "a powerful and indispensable auxiliary in our study of nature." The latter was, to be sure, more concerned to warn against their misuse than to show how they could be used. He did not advance the subject beyond Newton, and there were many who felt that his influence was retrograde. Had he not admonished: "Hypotheses must always be simply anticipations of what experience and reason could immediately have revealed had the circumstances been more favorable"?[75] Bernard's exposition was more specific and certainly more helpful.

A student who early recognized its value was Ernest Naville in his *Logique de l'hypothèse*.[76] Subsequently, another writer on the philosophy of science, Federigo Enriques, detected the striking similarity between the ideas of Bernard and of the English logician Jevons: "It is remarkable how minds of different training have come to the self-same result by various ways . . . . the different stages of this operation are similarly described by various authors, for example, by Bernard and by Stanley Jevons, who distinguish the preliminary observation, the hypothesis, the deduction, and the verification."[77] As Jevons's work appeared in 1873, several years after his French contemporary's, some measure of priority must be granted to Bernard. In addition to the parallel indicated by Enriques, it is worth noting that they agree also on the inadequacy of Baconian induction.[78] Jevons's analysis is of course more formal and methodical, as befits a specialist in logical theory. On the other hand, Bernard's reflections on scientific invention are derived not from bookish sources, but rise directly from his own rich fund of research experience.

Is Bernard's importance limited to that of a contemporary of Whewell, Mill, and Jevons, or does he also have something to offer our own age? Certainly his exposition does not sound old-fashioned when compared to the following statement in a standard text by Cohen and Nagel, *An Introduction to Logic and Scientific Method:* "We cannot take a single step forward in any inquiry unless we begin with a *suggested* explanation or solution of the difficulty which originated it. Such tentative explanations are suggested to us by something in the subject matter and by our previous knowledge."[79] More explicit testimony on the pertinence of Bernard's account of scientific discovery is supplied by a series of recent writers on the philosophy of science. Émile Meyerson has called attention to his remark that a method alone will not engender discoveries. The experimental method will not inspire new and fruitful ideas in men who lack them. "The idea is the seed; the method is the soil." An experimental fact may mean nothing, unless it is linked to a significant concept, or forms part of an inquiry combining experiment and theory.[80]

But though the experimentalist needs ideas, he must avoid fixed ideas and retain his freedom of intellectual maneuver. If we may borrow an expression made famous by a literary artist, André Gide's *disponibilité* suggests the state of mind which is to be desired.* Bernard's remarks on the subject have recently aroused the interest of the American philosophers J. R. Kantor and Max Black, the French scientific writers Pierre Vendryès and R. Taton.[81] Kantor notes his comments on the value of ignorance for discovery.[82] The word is perhaps misleading; it might be better to say *the open mind.* A related point is developed by Black in his discussion of fallibilism. "Bernard's fallibilism with respect to scientific theory—a doctrine held by many, but never, to my knowledge, stated better—will point the way to a more radical fallibilism with respect to the principles of scientific method." Among other statements, Black cites Bernard's striking phrase: "We must have robust faith and not believe."[83] A similar thought was expressed by Bernard's friend, the chemist Sainte-Claire Deville, with his maxim: "We must entertain theories without believing in them."[84] Modern logicians have spoken of replacing the criterion of verifiability with that of falsifiability. As Bernard observed: "We serve better through mistakes than through confusion." And again: "One cannot establish his ideas firmly without trying to destroy his own conclusions by means of counter-experiments."[85] Here we are already close to the principle of falsifiability, closer than we are with Bacon's *experimentum crucis,* or with Comte's simple recipe for verification.

---

*Another apt expression might be Keats's *negative capability.*

These considerations of the uses of ignorance raise the question of scientific determinism. In spite of the tendency nowadays to contest the validity of this concept, Black is inclined to agree that "Bernard's determinism, as he used it, can be shown to have been an active instrument of research and criticism." He goes on to say: "Bernard's robust faith in a deterministic order of nature fortifies him in a laborious but successful search for rational explanation." He questions, however, whether Bernard's determinism would have the same decisive influence in the research conditions of a later age. We must, writes Black, "be prepared to mix a little more skepticism with our faith than Bernard was prepared for."[86] But was Bernard's faith in determinism as naïve as Black implies? Certainly one cannot tax with a narrow dogmatism the scientist who could make statements like the following: "We must keep our freedom of mind and believe that what is absurd in terms of our theories is not always impossible." "Nature is inexhaustible."[87] Bernard's determinism was perhaps more attuned to the complexity of experience than he is given credit for by our contemporaries.

Another criticism made by Black involves Bernard's conception of observational data. Black finds unsophisticated the view that the observer is a passive photographer of nature, and that the facts of observation are simply given. Pure observation, asserts Black, is a myth. It might be countered that Bernard was as aware of this danger as we are. Did he not declare that a fact itself may be an abstraction? Was this not the gist of his criticism of the empiricism of his master Magendie? In any case, this was precisely the point made by Bergson in his Bernard lecture: "There is no difference between an observation well taken and a well-founded generalization."[88] Granted that Bergson may have had his own axe to grind, but he could not have cited Bernard if the latter had been a naïve realist or empiricist. On the other hand, if one were to make no distinction between the data of observation and the theoretical interpretation of the data, one would risk the opposite danger of subjectivism. Bernard's treatment of the matter was calculated to ward off this danger as well. He may have been no dialectician, yet he was alert to the perils of both Scylla and Charybdis.

The part of Bernard's exposition of scientific method which has been considered most nearly obsolete is undoubtedly his discussion of statistics. In an age when probability theory reigns supreme in the sub-atomic world, and when statistics make up a large part of social science, nothing might seem more old-fashioned than his assault on these techniques in his *Introduction*. Yet he does not lack defenders even in this respect. We have quoted (Chapter One) Kantor's remark that he did not object to statistics as investigative aids, but only to the replacement of medical data by numerical averages. The physician must treat human beings and not points on a distribution curve. A more outspoken indorsement of his attitude has come from Lancelot Hogben. Whether mainly right or wrong, Hogben's vigorous attack on alleged fallacies in statistics does suggest that Bernard's critique is not a dead issue and may still have validity in medical science. As Hogben declares: "If his comments on the use of averages were salutary in his own time, they are still more so in ours."[89] Such vindications of Bernard on the one matter which we might imagine history had decided against him serve to indicate the continued vitality of his teachings on scientific method.

At the same time we must recognize the limitations of his point of view on experimentation if it is extended too far beyond the realm of biological science. This was already explained by the physicist and historian Pierre Duhem early in the century. While lauding the cogency of Bernard's guiding rules for research in natural science, Duhem finds them insufficient for the more theoretical science of physics. After citing at length Bernard's prescription for the open mind so necessary for a physiologist, the author of *La Théorie physique; son objet et sa structure* shows the inadequacy of this prescription for the modern physics laboratory:

> But if the experimental method, as it has been described, is hard to practice, its logical analysis is very simple. It is otherwise when the theory which is to be checked against the facts is no longer a theory of Physiology, but a theory of Physics. Here, as a matter of fact,

> it can no longer be a question of leaving at the laboratory door the theory one wishes to test, for without it it is not possible to regulate a single instrument, or to interpret a single reading. . . .[90]

It is, of course, this complexity of the fact of observation which Black has in mind when he calls Bernard's conception unsophisticated. It is this complexity which has led to such developments in the philosophy of science as Percy Bridgman's operational approach. We can understand the indifference to Bernard of some contemporary philosophers of science, absorbed as they are in the intricate problems of interpretation raised by quantum physics and relativity. Nevertheless there remains an irreducible element of truth in Bernard's distinction between datum and theory which no theoretical symbolism can ever dissolve. The same could be said for his acceptance of scientific determinism. Here we anticipate one of the topics of the following section on philosophy in general. As for the scientists, they can still be guided and inspired by the example of that "robust faith without belief" which Claude Bernard held up to them.

III *Philosophy and General Ideas*

In so far as philosophy is concerned, the picture that Ernest Renan painted of Bernard in his Academy Discourse was that of the agnostic and seeker after truth: "He was of no school or sect. He sought the truth, and that was all. The heroes of the human mind are those who know how to be ignorant in order that posterity may know. All have not this courage."[91] Reading this eloquent salute, one wonders how much that was personal to himself Renan was ascribing to Bernard. How like Renan to mirror himself in an admired figure! In his famous letter to Berthelot, entitled "Les Sciences de la nature et les sciences historiques" (1863), he had expressed his regret at having only one life to devote to knowledge, and at being unable to lead also the life of a natural scientist like his friends Berthelot and Bernard.[92] In 1848, when writing *The Future of Science (L'Avenir de la science),* he had been less certain of the supreme value of natural science.[93] But in retrospect, in *Memories of Childhood and Youth (Souvenirs d'enfance et de jeunesse)* (1883), he voiced the same sense of a missed vocation, and, incidentally, revealed how deeply impressed he had been by Bernard's work in general physiology: ". . . it is above all through general physiology that we touch the secret of being, of the world, of God, as we may wish to call it."[94] Here at least, in paying his respects to the late physiologist, he could momentarily project himself into such a career.

He was capable, in a less ceremonial context, of poking gentle fun at the ingenuous *savant* who, in an off moment, once dismissed sexual love as an easily explained derivative of nutrition.[95] Such things were not, of course, for an Address of Reception to the French Academy, in which the new member was expected to deliver a dignified eulogy of his predecessor. A eulogy it is, but how much more genuine, and more intrinsically valuable, than the usual run of Academic Discourses! Renan throws into relief the enduring elements of Bernard's teaching: the necessary objectivity of the scientist, the validity of determinism in the organic realm, the conquering role of science— "être maître de la nature"; and finally, the separation between the real and the ideal. In the unfolding of this last theme, we need not ask how much was Bernard's, how much was Renan's. It was a theme which united them all, Renan, Bernard, as well as Berthelot, against the simplistic affirmations of the Positivist school.[96] In *The Future of Science,* Renan had exclaimed: "If human nature were such as M. Comte conceives it, all refined souls would rush to suicide. It would not be worth one's trouble to turn such an insignificant crank-handle . . . . The misfortune of M. Comte is to have a system."[97] More hackneyed in style yet similar in meaning is Bernard's rejoinder to Comte's *Positive Philosophy:* "Indeed the positive stage as Comte understands it will be the reign of sheer rationalism, the reign of the head and the death of the heart. That is not possible. Men formed thus by science are moral monsters."[98] Both unpublished during Bernard's lifetime, these passages reveal a notable affinity. It is almost like overhearing a conversation between the two men to read this comment in *Memories of Childhood and Youth:* "I felt a kind of irritation seeing the exaggerated reputation of Auguste Comte, elevated to great man of the first rank for having said in bad French what all scientific minds for two hundred years had seen as clearly as he."[99] Here are the very accents of the veiled references to Comte we have studied in the *Introduction to Experimental Medicine*.

Some typical followers of Renan were Anatole France, Jules de Gaultier, and Remy de Gourmont. How did they look upon Bernard? Without the personal contact enjoyed by Renan, they had little occasion to express themselves concerning Bernard, who had after all no part in that heritage of skepticism and dilettantism they took over from their master. In his Renanian *Garden of Epicurus (Jardin d'Épicure)*, Anatole France imagines Bernard in the Elysian Fields among the sages vainly trying to define the *soul*. He has Bernard replying to Pyrrho's question "What is life?" with his familiar phrase "La vie c'est la mort." As for the question "What is death?" there is not one of these illustrious *dead* who can answer.[100] The same breviary of skepticism has the aphorism: "Ignorance is the necessary condition, I do not say for happiness, but for existence itself. If we knew everything, we could not endure life for a single hour."[101] We are reminded of Bernard's remark, in his notes on Comte: "When man knows everything, he will cease to exist."[102] But his notion of the uses of ignorance is, as we have seen, entirely different. He has nothing in common with this *fin-de-siècle* world-weariness, fortunately a passing mood even with Anatole France.

On the other hand, the skeptical turn Renan had given to Bernard's thought does have a connection with the philosophy of Jules de Gaultier. The inventor of Bovarysm explicitly mentions Bernard as a scientist endowed with philosophic understanding who encouraged him in his thesis of the uncertainty of human knowledge. When man thinks himself able to attain absolute knowledge, he is a victim of the illusion exemplified in a meaner form by Emma Bovary—the tendency to see himself as other than he is. Bernard's warning about the provisional character of theories, his emphasis on the relative and the approximate, become for Gaultier an invitation to espouse a radical relativism which was certainly not part of the intention. For Gaultier, then, the notions of science and truth become mutually exclusive.[103] We are surprised to find the *Introduction to Experimental Medicine* serving as a steppingstone in Gaultier's debonair progress from Kant to Nietzsche, to an esthetic illusionism *sans* the Will to Power.[104] The science that had aimed at mastering nature has turned into a spectator sport!

Although Gaultier's kindred spirit, Remy de Gourmont, was an admirer of Bernard, one hesitates at singling him out as a disciple.[105] This assiduous reader of science makes only a handful of references to our physiologist. There is in common between Bernard and the later, not the early Symbolist Gourmont, a form of scientific positivism, but that is hardly enough to mark him as a follower. In one place he describes him as a vitalist, though of a type far removed from Bichat.[106] The short piece in *Nouvelles Dissociations* entitled "Claude Bernard" merely puts in a nutshell the familiar points that Bernard had brought the experimental method into medicine and had based physiology on determinism. Does Bernard have a philosophy? Gourmont's answer is short and simple: Yes—determinism. But the final tribute has, considering its date (1913), a commonplace ring: "He is a great mind, a great creator of truths, the master, the Descartes of the experimental scientific method."[107]

Gourmont wrote essays on Quinton's theory of the constancy of the vital milieu, which was inspired by Bernard's concept of the internal environment.[108] The idea is dimly reflected even in that mélange of Renanian dialogue and erotic dream called *A Night in the Luxembourg (Une Nuit au Luxembourg).*[109] But nowhere does the "encyclopedic mind" of Gourmont disclose any awareness of the provenance. That he could be so enchanted by Quinton's hypothesis—he ranked Quinton with Darwin—and yet never suspect its derivation from the *milieu intérieur* is a striking example of his generation's blindness to the real seminal value of Bernard's discovery.

If Gourmont belongs in the relativist current coming from Renan, he does not, like his friend Gaultier, stress the relativist aspect of Bernard. He views him as a determinist. The deterministic strand leads us back naturally to Renan's contemporary Hippolyte Taine. His thought was crystallized in the famous phrase from the Introduction to his *History of English Literature:* "Vice and virtue are products like sugar and sulphuric acid." To what extent was Taine beholden to Bernard? The question has seemed to certain writers an easy one to answer. Thus Pierre Lamy asserts: "Through Taine, Claude Bernard holds sway over the entire intellectual movement whose orientation was fixed by the preface to the *History of English Literature*."[110] In a book on Taine, P. V. Rubow states the same opinion: "This great scientist was for Taine and his generation a guiding star and his *Introduction to the Study of Experimental Medicine* was their bedside book."[111] Yet Taine might have been surprised to be treated as a follower of Bernard. He studied some physiology in the 1850's just when Bernard was making his outstanding discoveries. Taine was not strongly impressed. Was he bumptious or merely hasty and impatient when he described Bernard's Sorbonne lectures as "Commonplaces painfully delivered by a man who does not know how to talk."[112] In the following decade he is reported to have had frequent contacts with Bernard, Vulpian, and Charles Robin.[113] For all that, his book *De l'Intelligence* (1870) contains hardly a reference to Bernard's physiological investigations, although Johannes Müller and Helmholtz come in for repeated mention. This is quite fitting, especially in view of Helmholtz's work on sensation, which was much closer to Taine's main subject.

The fact is that Taine's determinism was nurtured much more by the philosophers Spinoza and Hegel, the English associationists, even the novelist Balzac and the Positivist Comte than it was by Bernard, whose great book appeared after the foundations of Taine's system had been laid down.[114] According to Étienne Vacherot, he looked askance at Bernard's *idée directrice* and did not approve of this intrusion of metaphysics into science. As Vacherot would have it, Bernard was not mechanist enough for Taine. With Vacherot's penchant for teleology, it was natural for him to feel that Bernard was more philosophical than Taine.[115] Nevertheless, Taine welcomed the statement of scientific determinism set forth in the *Introduction to Experimental Medicine,* and adopted the axiom that if conditions are identical, phenomena are identical. This does not mean that Bernard had any decisive effect on Taine's treatise on the mind. The author of *De l'Intelligence* was too much the analyst of abstractions, too little the experimentalist, to do more than point the way for those like Ribot whose psychology would be experimental as well as determinist. Taine's use of Bernard's texts is interesting in another way. He utilizes them to re-enforce the thesis that man's conception of the world, while conforming with the structure of the mind, is also in accord with the structure of the world.[116] He stops short of the extreme position of Lachelier who, we recall, considers natural law to be a proof of idealism. Is there a certain naïveté in Taine's confidence in the uniformity of nature? Such is the opinion of Alexander Bain in his criticism of Taine, and, by implication, of Bernard: "In the law of nature they say today and tomorrow are the same. . . . Does this get us out of our difficulty? It does by begging the question that time and space are not conditions of cause and effect."[117] On an issue of this kind, a philosopher may be held more severely to account than a scientist who disclaims philosophical ambitions. The uniformity of nature was an inseparable part of Bernard's robust faith as an experimentalist, and it does seem to be vindicated by results, regardless of anyone's refined epistemological objections.

It was inevitable that this determinism, for all Bernard's efforts to limit it to science, would be interpreted by some readers in a broader sense. His very reservations could be mistaken for weakness. In that free-swinging attack on what its author called *Le stupide XIXe Siècle,* this determinism is treated as a stunted caricature of positivism. Léon Daudet is a son in whom his father's mellow wine had turned to vinegar—which he took for vitriol. In another book *Les Morticoles* he had assailed medical men even more violently than did Maupassant in *Mont-Oriol.* Thus we are less surprised than bemused by his sarcasm. On a different plane, he seems to be trying to outdo his former colleague in the Action Française, Pierre Lasserre, whose onslaught on *Le Romantisme français* had shaken the Sorbonne around 1907. The brimstone that Daudet heaped upon the first decades of the Third Republic has cooled by now, but it is still diverting to recall some of his comments: "The dull determinism of a Claude Bernard (the poverty of which contrasts with his bold experiments) encourages the trivialities of a Zola."[118] He extends his condemnation not only to Bernard and Zola but to the entire period: "Towards the close of this strange and dismal epoch, philosophy appeared as a mere phosphorescence of biological science, and of medical science, whose decrepitude people failed to realize."[119] This sniping was part of a broad campaign conducted by the Action Française against what they regarded as the official culture of the despised Third Republic.

If there was anyone who thought that philosophy was a mere phosphorescence of biology, it might have been Zola; it certainly was not Bernard. The technical name for such a doctrine is, of course, epiphenomenalism. Around the turn of the century, its best-known proponent was undoubtedly Félix Le Dantec. This writer, incidentally, is an avowed "scientiste," thus defying those like Brunetière who were announcing the "bankruptcy of science." According to Le Dantec, philosophy is valid only in so far as it coincides with science.[120] In matters of physiology, he took issue more than once with Bernard, notably in repudiating the latter's theory that irritability is a basic property of life.[121] Le Dantec's thoroughgoing mechanistic bent led him to a determinism that was more rigorous than that of Bernard.[122] Of the many books of this prolific author, there is one written in a lighter and more informal manner which is still highly readable today. It is a collection of dialogues entitled *Le Conflit*. The main speaker is Fabrice Tacaud, a physiologist and free-thinker, who debates with his clerical friend such problems as free will, the origin of life, and the meaning of death. Judging by this book, Le Dantec must have cut his teeth on the writings of Bernard, if we can assume that Tacaud is his *alter ego*. Tacaud relates how as a young man he had studiously sought the last word on physiology in Bernard, especially in the *Phénomènes de la vie*. Unfortunately, though he read it a dozen times, he was disappointed by its obscurities and contradictions.[123] Knowing something of Le Dantec's decidedly mechanistic views, we can understand Tacaud's dissatisfaction with Bernard's less doctrinaire formulations of vital phenomena.

Up to now, we have seen how Bernard's relativism and determinism are reflected in writers from Renan and Taine down to Gaultier and Le Dantec, respectively. These were typical themes of the late nineteenth century. As we enter the twentieth, certain more novel implications, unnoticed before, now come into perspective. This is the age of Bergson and Poincaré in France, of Mach in Germany, of James in America. Boutroux's concept of the contingency of natural law, Bergson's philosophy of intuition, Mach's critical empiricism, James's pragmatism, make up a climate quite unlike that which prevailed in the days of Taine and Spencer. In some ways, Bernard turns out to be less timebound than his contemporaries. It is true that a Bergsonian like Georges Sorel regards him as a representative man of that earlier, more confident age. Yet it is from Bernard's theory of experimental method that Sorel takes his departure to end up in a conventionalism as radical as that of Duhem or Poincaré. Experimental science constructs an artificial nature to replace "natural" nature.[124] This split between science and nature is already a far cry from Bernard. Similarly, Bernard's comparison of hypotheses to instruments of the mind becomes for Poincaré a concept of hypotheses as virtually arbitrary mental constructs. Following Bernard, Poincaré showed that they are indispensable for science. But unlike Bernard, he did not think that any particular hypothesis is privileged. The choice between Euclidean and some non-Euclidean geometry, for example, may depend no longer on observation but on criteria of convenience, simplicity, and elegance.[125] The difference between Bernard's and Poincaré's conceptions is partly a difference between an observational science like biology and an abstract science like mathematics.

It is striking to find Bernard's imprint on a philosophy as remote from his characteristic rationalist and determinist position as is the intuitionism of Bergson. The latter's tribute at the centenary of the scientist's birth is more than a ceremonial offering of praise. It may be compared for its urbanity and fineness of appreciation to Renan's Academic Address, but it has a further significance in that it uncovers the influence of Bernard at the very roots of Bergson's thought. For Bergson, Bernard is important not only because he clarified the relation between fact and idea in experimental research, not only because he refuted both "vital force" and mechanism, but also because he knew that reality is more complex than intelligence can conceive.[126]

That Bergson's attack on reason carried the implications of that truth far beyond Bernard's intention does not cancel out the latter's historical role. As Bergson declares: "As we advance farther and farther along the way we have taken, we must always remember that Claude Bernard helped to open it."[127]

In a more particular way, the scientist seems to have inspired certain passages of *Creative Evolution (L'Évolution créatrice)*. This is worth noting because it involves nothing less than the concept of the inner environment. The physiology of the autonomic nervous system is one of the foundations of Bergson's biological philosophy. We have referred above to Barcroft's experimental verification of Bernard's maxim: "The fixity of the internal environment is the condition necessary for a free life." Such was the line taken by Bergson in developing his theory of creative evolution: "A higher organism is . . . a sensory-motor system installed over apparatus of digestion, respiration, circulation, secretion, etc., whose function is . . . to create for it a constant internal environment."[128] Returning to the same thought later in the book, he writes: "The latter have as function to clean, repair, protect the organism and to render it as independent as possible of external circumstances, but above all to supply it with the energy which it is to expend in movements."[129] We immediately recall such statements as the following from Bernard's *Introduction to Experimental Medicine:* "The organism is only a living machine constructed in such a fashion that there are . . . functions, protecting the organic elements putting materials of life in storage and maintaining . . . the conditions indispensable for vital activity."[130] The new element which Bergson introduces is the idea of creative evolution, of the life drive or *élan vital*. The constancy of the inner milieu might be compared to a springboard from which the *élan vital* launches into an open future.

The Bergsonian vitalist *mystique* has little in common with Bernard's approach to the phenomena of life. This fact Bergson clearly recognized: "Claude Bernard did not give us, nor did he try to give us, a metaphysics of life."[131] Thus we have no warrant for associating Bernard with these modern "religions" like the biological metaphysics of Bergson or the Life-Force God of

George Bernard Shaw. The antivivisectionist barbs in the preface
of *Back to Methuselah* indicate that Shaw was worlds removed
from a laboratory scientist like Claude Bernard. Yet Bernard
gave vent in a meditative mood to speculations reminiscent of
Samuel Butler, so often called a forerunner of Bergson and
Shaw. In a letter to Mme Raffalovich, quoted in part by Renan,
Bernard wrote in 1876:

> I should like to examine the question whether one could
> characterize life by memory . . . . Everything existing has
> the memory of a previous state. I once wrote: the germ
> retains the memory or recollection of the organism to
> which it belonged before reproducing it. Memory is
> thus identified with growth which is a fundamental
> character of the living being. Habit also is linked with
> the same order of phenomena, and living things alone
> are capable of it. In short, in any manifestation of life,
> nature repeats a lesson which it has learned and which
> it remembers more or less well.[132]

It is a striking coincidence that Butler was almost simultaneously
framing his own idea that the reproductive germ carries a stock
of ancestral memories which govern the growth of the offspring.
A hint of this notion occurs as early as 1867 in the article referred
to by Bernard, "Le Problème de la physiologie générale."[133] In
1870 Ewald Hering delivered a lecture entitled "Memory as a
Universal Function of Organized Matter," in which he expounded his conception of memory as embracing involuntary
and unconscious activities. In a subsequent book, Butler denied
any knowledge of Hering's work when he wrote *Life and Habit*
(1877), but he does not even mention Bernard.[134] In any case,
Bernard's approach to the question was different from that of
Butler. The physiologist was speculating on the possibility of
producing new species by "teaching nature a new lesson." "It
is still my old idea of remaking living things not by the spontaneous generation some have dreamed of, but by the repetition
of organic phenomena of which nature preserves the secret."[135]
He was somewhat apologetic of these "nebulous divagations,"
but hoped that one day science would make them clearer. Nothing could indicate better the difference between Bernard and the

iconoclastic Butler. The one meant to use the idea as a guiding hypothesis for experimental test; the other elaborated it into a quasi-religious system to challenge Darwinian evolution.

Bernard and Bergson belong, in the main, to separate currents of thought, the rival traditions of Cartesian and Romantic philosophy. Bernard's campaign against the vitalism of Bichat and the *Naturphilosophie* of Schelling impugned some of the very sources of Bergsonism.[136] How then can we explain Bergson's sympathetic attitude toward Bernard? How did Bernard escape the sort of criticism which Bergson directed against contemporaries like Spencer and Taine? It is no doubt largely because Bergson could interpret certain ideas of Bernard in a pragmatist, if not an intuitionist sense. The scientist's account of discovery as derived from hints and hunches seemed to point to Bergsonian intuition. And Bernard's distrust of ready-made formulae seemed to accord with Bergson's distrust of the logical intellect. In a wartime essay on French philosophy, Bergson described the scientific process as a collaboration of idea and fact. He thought this implied a gap between man's logic and nature's logic. "On this point, and on several others, Claude Bernard anticipated the 'pragmatist' theorists of science."[137] Bergson was referring to such anticipations as Bernard's repeated comparison of theories with intellectual instruments.

In the running battle which the defender of the intellect, Julien Benda, carried on against his favorite enemy, Bergson, the exact meaning of Bernard's statements was more than once a bone of contention. Benda took issue immediately with Bergson's description of Bernard as a pragmatist.[138] Somewhat earlier, he had contested the Bergsonian interpretation of Bernard's *sentiment*. There are, he admits, two kinds of intelligence, the slow, discursive type and the quick, intuitive one. He charged Bergson with being unfair to *intelligence* by giving that name only to the first kind, while reserving *intuition* for the second. Bernard's "sentiment de l'esprit," contended Benda, is not the same as *feeling*.[139] This uncompromising rationalist was also able to find support in Bernard against Bergsonian indeterminism. Discussing some constants in modern scientific theory, he compares Einstein's determinism to Bernard's maxim: "Vous devez croire au déterminisme, même non formulable."[140] ("You must believe in determinism, even if it cannot be formulated.") Benda's comments when taken in conjunction with those of Bergson enable us to define the relationship of Bernard to the question of pragmatism. When Bernard calls theories "instruments" in the search for truth, when he asserts that man can do more than he knows, when he declares that science humbles our pride while increasing our power, he might almost be setting up a program for pragmatism. There is a remarkable affinity between such thoughts and the following statement of William James:

> The pragmatic method . . . appears less as a solution than as a program for more work, . . . as an indication of the ways in which existing realities may be changed. *Theories thus become instruments, not answers to enigmas in which we can rest.* Pragmatism being nothing essentially new . . . agrees with nominalism, for instance, in always appealing to particulars; with utilitarianism in emphasizing practical aspects; with positivism in its disdain for verbal solutions, useless and metaphysical abstractions.

But James's next remark immediately sets us straight, for he says: "All these, you see, are anti-intellectualist tendencies."[141] Bernard would have agreed with everything but this. For he remained, after all, faithful to rationalism, "même non formulable." Moreover, he did not favor the voluntaristic element of pragmatism.

Did Bernard have a part in the origins of the pragmatist movement? We know that James, while still in his physiologist stage, praised the *Introduction to Experimental Medicine* and favorably reviewed the *Rapport*. But the silence he maintained afterwards on Bernard would suggest that Bernard's scattered phrases faded in his memory into anonymity, to merge with a host of other influences impelling him in the same direction. As for the "father" of the school, Charles Peirce, his offhanded refutation of Bernard's "nominalism" does not indicate any positive influence. We are justified in saying, not that Bernard anticipated pragmatism—for he was no pragmatist—but that he was original enough to produce ideas that could make the fortune of later thinkers without stepping out of his role as a representative of experimental rationalism. What distinguished him from traditional rationalism was his recognition that "the aim of mankind is no longer passive contemplation but progress and action."

Citing this maxim in a preceding chapter, we observed how similar it is both to some statements of John Dewey and to a well-known pronouncement of Karl Marx: "Heretofore the philosophers have explained nature; now the thing to do is to change it." Thus it is not surprising that some students of Marxist inspiration have displayed an interest in Bernard. What is surprising is that they have displayed so little. This interest in Bernard is a relatively recent development and largely confined to the French. Marx's collaborator Engels does not appear to have noticed the scientist, even in his works dealing with biology. The French Marxist Paul Lafargue did so, but only incidentally, in a review of Zola, charging the novelist with misuse of Bernard's authority in calling himself a disciple of the physiologist in *Le Roman expérimental*.[142] The political conformity of Napoleon the Third's appointee to the Senate was not calculated to attract the attention of the earlier Marxians. A concise statement from an evidently authorized source is that of Lucy Prenant in a lecture on "Marx et Comte" (1935). This exposé of the shortcomings of Comte when measured against Marx presents Bernard, in passing, as a better positivist than Comte. Mme Prenant welcomes Bernard's confidence in science, his clarification of the relation between theory and practice in experiment, and his sense of the active character of scientific thought. She detects a hint of dialectical materialism in certain statements in which he seems to be groping toward a view which dissolves *things* into *processes*. But she takes him severely to task for his agnostic tendencies, his concessions to teleology and his complaisant attitude toward ideal hypotheses.[143] Signs of a more sympathetic approach to Bernard on the part of French adepts of Marxism have appeared since the Second World War, and one may predict that fuller studies will be forthcoming from that direction.[144]

In so far as the different streams of the Hegelian tradition are concerned, interest in Bernard has not been confined to these

"Hegelians of the Left." René Berthelot, son of Bernard's friend Marcellin Berthelot, can be taken as representative of the direct Hegelian lineage. In a critique of pragmatism, Berthelot argues that the "pragmatist" Nietzsche put together a crude mixture of vitalism and mechanism without ever being able to bring these disparate elements into a proper synthesis. In contrast, Berthelot points to the development by Lamarck, Bernard, Helmholtz, and Darwin of a broader and more flexible conception of mechanism which need not resort to a radical spontaneity that would spell the failure of determinism. Using Hegelian terms, he generalizes Bernard's experimental reasoning into a dialectical attitude of the mind, a dialectical conception of truth.[145] Though it is only incidental to Berthelot's main discussion, such a translation into Hegelian language may be contrasted with Bergson's interpretation of Bernard as a "pragmatist."

A French writer on philosophy has declared that Bernard exerted little influence on philosophical thought.[146] Doubtless it is true that his influence was neither profound nor epoch-making. Yet everything considered, one must be impressed by the variety of philosophical idioms into which their proponents have translated the thoughts of this physiologist who never claimed to be a philosopher. As we have seen, these interpretations cover a large part of the philosophical spectrum, from the materialist Letourneau, the idealist Caro, and the Neo-Thomist Sertillanges to Renanian skeptics like Gaultier, to Hegelians Right and Left, to the irrationalist Bergson. The urge felt by so many to construe his thinking in their terms was prompted in part by the ambiguities of his own language. To paraphrase Bernard himself, this was an instrument that had been worn down by use. It had become dulled in the hands of the eclectics who dominated French education during his youth. Yet there is another reason for the wide interest aroused by his writings: the challenge presented by original insights striving for expression, of new ideas caught in the toils of the old, but breaking free again and again to emerge in such arresting forms as these: "It is not enough to remain a passive spectator of good and evil, enjoying one and avoiding the other. Modern thought aspires to a greater role: it seeks the causes . . . it wants in short to dominate good and evil."[147]

CHAPTER Six

Claude Bernard and Literature

LE CORPS est un laboratoire
Où Lavoisier porta le jour;
À toi, Claude Bernard, la gloire
De l'illuminer à ton tour!
Ton œil en perce les arcanes
D'un regard subtil, vaste et sûr.
Du plus rebelle des organes
Tu surprends enfin l'œuvre obscur.
Tu rends visible chez la plante
Par de factices pâmoisons
La vie en elle somnolente,
Humaine sous d'humbles cloisons.

118 CLAUDE BERNARD

Tes savants et beaux artifices
Contraignent même les poisons
À rendre aux mortels des services.

Sully Prudhomme: *Le Bonheur*[1]*

These lines come from the poet's rhymed catalog of scientific progress in his now little-heeded version of the Faustian theme. Sully Prudhomme's ambition to create a poetry of science was not matched by his imaginative powers. His well-meant tribute to Bernard might provide the clinching demonstration that only a poetry as prosaic as his could even pretend to deal with such refractory topics. In any case, his effort is an isolated one, an exception that proves that Bernard's work was of a nature not calculated to influence poetry. He was important, not for the Literature of Power, but for the Literature of Knowledge. Thus our study reduces itself to an examination of Bernard's impact on the novel.

Claude Bernard was not, of course, the fountainhead of the influence of biology in literature. One recalls the exclamation of Sainte-Beuve upon reading *Madame Bovary* (1857): "Anatomists and physiologists, I meet you everywhere!"[2] Obviously, "physiology" had become a catchword and a sign of the times. So it is on a stage already trod by other actors that Bernard came to play his role in literature. When his leading position in science became generally known, he fell heir to a stereotype which public opinion attached to his name. Indicative of this are the references in the Goncourt *Journal*. Another example could be found in Russian fiction of the period. The hero of Turgenev's novel *Fathers and Sons* (1863) is Bazarov, the prototype of the Physiologist in fiction. There is no mention of Claude Bernard. But when Dostoyevsky produces *The Brothers Karamazov*

---

*The body's a laboratory
Lit up by Lavoisier;
For you, Bernard, the glory
Of lighting it today!
You pierce its secret places
With sharp and steady view.
Of the most elusive organs
You surprise the hidden clue.

You disclose within the plant,
Contriving curious spell,
The life there somnolent,
Humanlike in humble cell.
Your skillful artifice can
Even poisons compel
To be of help to man.

(1880), Bernard has already become a sort of *bête noire*, the object of Dmitri's prejudice and scorn. It is as if Bernard had inherited the dislike which Dostoyevsky feels for the Bazarovs.[3] For others, too, he exemplifies the type of the heartless scientist. One of the Parnassians, Louis Ménard, feels so strongly about vivisection that he takes sides with Mme Bernard against her husband. Consider his amazing remark in the *Rêveries d'un païen mystique:* "Claude Bernard's widow has opened a home for dogs to make amends for the crimes of experimental physiology. On Judgment Day, this offering will weigh more in the awesome balance than all the discoveries of her husband."[4] A poet more sympathetic toward science, Sully Prudhomme, could ask in almost the same spirit:

> Et quel amour goûter, quand dans la chair vivante
> Un froid naturaliste enfonce le scalpel,
> Et qu'on entend hurler d'angoisse et d'épouvante
> La victime, aux dieux sourds poussant un rauque appel?[5]

> ("And what love savor, when into the living flesh
> A cold naturalist plunges the scalpel
> And one hears howling with anguish and terror
> The victim, throwing to deaf gods a hoarse appeal?")

Just as Bazarov was called a nihilist, Bernard was to be implicitly charged with furthering immoralism by Edouard Rod in his *Idées morales du temps présent.*[6] His memory was not to be immune from the suspicion that he favored human vivisection, like the absurd "scientist" Dr. Donnat of François de Curel's play *La Nouvelle Idole.*[7]

Professor Olmsted discovered a tangential influence of Bernard on the once prominent Second Empire novelist Edmond About. Having heard the physiologist explaining the revival of rotifera after prolonged desiccation, About took it into his head to apply this motif to man in his story of *The Man with the Broken Ear (L'Homme à l'oreille cassée).* This piece of "science-fiction" turns on the resuscitation after fifty years of the mummy of an army officer frozen in Napoleon's Russian campaign. Finally revived by the German scientist of the story, the officer awakes to utter a feeble "Vive l'Empereur!" and then expires.[8] (This egregious bit of nonsense has itself been recently "revived" by an alleged scientist in California who, according to newspaper report, proposed a similar procedure to be used in time of unemployment—putting the surplus labor force literally into cold storage until such time as they might be needed.) Obviously these incongruities have nothing to do with the work of Bernard. They are in an area which belongs to the domain of folk superstition or, as Sir Thomas Browne termed it, *pseudodoxia epidemica.*

To some extent our hindsight has made Bernard's role seem more decisive than it actually was. Thus the Goncourt brothers, for all their *Journal* entries on Bernard, owed little or nothing to him in "physiological" novels like *Germinie Lacerteux* (1864).[9] Flaubert did not require his example when writing *Madame Bovary,* and there is no discernible echo of Bernard's doctrines in the misadventures in science of Bouvard and Pécuchet. The novelist's high regard for Bernard is, however, undeniable. One indication is the letter encouraging his niece Caroline to attend the physiologist's lectures.[10] The most famous instance of Bernard's impact upon literature, of course, is the case of Émile Zola.

So much has been published on Zola's conception of the "experimental novel" that it is fitting to limit ourselves here to a rather condensed outline of the subject. It is evident that Zola's transliteration of Bernard's experimental scientist into the "experimental novelist" was something of an afterthought. He had already marked out his path years before in such writings as *Thérèse Raquin.* In his preface to the second edition of this novel, he dwelt on his scientific aims in language which only the lack of a word distinguishes from his subsequently presented theory of the experimental novel: "I have but one desire: given a powerful man and an unsated woman, to cast them into a violent drama and scrupulously note down the sensations and actions of these creatures."[11] The profound modification of the organism under the pressure of environment and circumstance: that was his objective in *Thérèse Raquin,* just as it was to be formulated later.[12] It would seem that he sought in Bernard the authority which attacks on his "physiological" novels made him think he needed.

When *Nana* first appeared, as a serial in *Le Voltaire,* it was prefaced by the essay "Le Roman expérimental." His recourse to the celebrated work of Claude Bernard was undoubtedly prompted by the public attention devoted to the scientist upon his death. No specific allusions to Bernard are to be found in Zola's writings prior to 1878. The assertion of Henry Céard that Zola did not study Bernard until 1879 has been accepted as authoritative.[13] The *Introduction to Experimental Medicine* is no longer regarded as having inspired the Rougon-Macquart cycle from its inception.

Nevertheless, the essay "Le Roman expérimental" is more than a polemic based on a handful of hastily gathered quotations. Perhaps it did not entirely deserve the rain of ridicule which fell upon it, the mocking verses and the sneering reviews.[14] Although the introductory outline is merely a transcription of Bernard's chapter-headings, the body of the article reveals a studious reading of the book. The half a hundred citations leave unturned only the more technical portions. Zola divides his essay into five parts. In the first he reviews Bernard's comparison of the observer and the experimenter, and argues that the novelist too follows the observational and the experimental method. Here he introduces his celebrated sophism to the effect that when a novelist like Balzac sets a character into motion he is performing an experiment fundamentally no different from a laboratory investigation. In Zola's second chapter we learn that experimentation is legitimate not only in physical science but also in the field of vital phenomena. Here Zola puts forth his claim that the experimental novel is the culmination of this advance of science from the inorganic to the organic realm. In his third section he assumes on behalf of the modern novel the task Bernard had undertaken in the name of medical science: to study phenomena in order to master them. Thus the novelist places his ideal of human betterment through science under the auspices of Claude Bernard. The next chapter, basing itself on the progress of medicine from art to science, calls upon young writers to free themselves from the sway of idealism and to apply the scientific method in literature. Only in his fifth and final section does Zola take issue with his mentor. For Bernard upholds precisely the conventional idealistic view of artists and writers that his disciple has been at pains to combat! How could Zola agree that art is personal, only science is impersonal?[15]

Almost every commentator on Zola's essay has smiled at the presumption of the novelist who fancies he is conducting experiments when he is merely contriving plots and putting invented characters into fictitious settings. One who smiled was Anatole France. In a superficial witticism, he compares Zola, not to Bernard, but to Magendie who prided himself on working without a preconceived idea: "The leader of this literary school who talks so much of experiments, reminds us of a well-known physiologist . . . the *bonhomme* Magendie who experimented a great deal to no advantage." But Zola is in fact closer to Hippolyte Taine cross-matching his "petits faits vrais" than he is to either Magendie or Claude Bernard. Was he conscious of the falseness of the analogy? We know that he paid no heed to Céard's warning that he was presenting a fallacy.[16] If he had any misgivings, he brushed them aside. But the essay would have gained in logical cogency what it might have lost in a certain crude publicity value, if Zola had advanced the analogy as simply a suggestive parallel.

The aftermath of Bernard's death found Zola adverting once again to the example of the great physiologist. In his "Letter to Youth," he enshrines him as the representative man of the age. He takes his cue from the tribute which Renan pronounced upon succeeding to Bernard's chair in the Academy. Somewhat speciously, Zola sets up the scientist in opposition to the idealist Renan and the lyricist Victor Hugo. "Renan is only a charmer, a dreamer behind the times; the strength of the age is with Bernard."[17] It is a rather callow attack on the author of *The Future of Science,* but of course Zola is unaware of the optimistic manifesto on science reposing still unprinted in Renan's desk drawer.

Zola was not to forget Bernard in a later phase of his career. We recall that he planned to model his character Dr. Pascal upon the author of the *Introduction to Experimental Medicine.* Though he gave up the notion, there still remains in *Le docteur Pascal* some trace of this earlier project. Dr. Pascal is, to be sure, a student of heredity who is more interested in the evolutionists Darwin, Haeckel, and Weismann than he is in the follower of Magendie. But it was the personal life of Bernard that intrigued Zola. The separation of Bernard and Mme Bernard occurred the same year as his reception into the Academy, in other words just when he was becoming widely known. In this same year of 1869, the Goncourts are found chuckling in their *Journal* over the "tueur de Dieu" who had married a bigot.[18] By coincidence, it is to the surviving brother Edmond that Zola confides a score of years later that he is thinking of portraying a scientist plagued with a narrow-minded spouse. Zola is now working on *L'Argent* and *La Débâcle* before taking up *Le docteur Pascal*. He tells Goncourt:

> The book which interests me, which attracts me, is the last one, in which I will present a scientist . . . . I am tempted to model him after Claude Bernard, getting access to his papers and letters. It will be amusing . . . I will make a scientist married to a backward, bigoted woman, who will destroy his researches as he works.[19]

What dissuaded Zola from carrying out this plan? Certainly it was not out of consideration for the privacy of a respected *savant*. In 1893 after the book had appeared, he gave the following explanation to an interviewer: "I had thought of utilizing certain details furnished me on the intimate sufferings of Claude Bernard; but the requirements of my story, the framework in which I must enclose it, did not permit me to employ them as I had wished. Only fragments of them will be found in my book."[20] It is evident that Bernard's life would not have served Zola's purpose. The Rougon-Macquart cycle required a scientist preoccupied with heredity who would weave together in his dossiers the scattered strands of the family destinies. As for the odd romance between the elderly uncle Pascal and his niece Clotilde, and how it reflects Zola's own "new life" with young Jeanne Rozerot,[21] that is not our affair, for it has no connection with Claude Bernard.

The character of Dr. Pascal had actually been conceived years before Zola ever thought of modeling him after Bernard.

Already appearing in the first of the series, *La Fortune des Rougon* (1871), Pascal is described as having settled in the provinces after medical studies in Paris. His modest practice leaves him ample time to pursue his investigation of heredity, which has become for him almost an obsession. The author is not well advised in placing a "pioneer" of science in an environment without advantages for genuine scientific research. The parallels with the life of Bernard occur only in the last of the series, *Le docteur Pascal*. The mother of Pascal, Félicité, is somewhat reminiscent of Mme Bernard. Both were disappointed at the failure of son or husband to acquire a rich practice. Mme Bernard showed an active hostility toward her husband's research. Félicité, aided by the servant, goes much farther: she burns the doctor's research notes upon his death. Yet she does not do this in a fever of obscurantism, but from anxiety over the family skeletons that might come tumbling out.

One might compare Bernard's eloquent description of the scientist's stubborn quest for truth, given in the closing chapter of his *Introduction*, with a similar picture of Dr. Pascal, painted by Zola. It is a lofty theme, but too commonplace to constitute a significant parallel. Zola had, in fact, copied this picture from the sketch of Renan made, of all people, by the Viscount de Vogüé.[22] A more definite link is Dr. Pascal's attitude toward medicine, clearly reflecting Bernard's own: "Empiricism reduced him to despair. If medicine was not an experimental science but an art, he remained perplexed and anxious before the infinite complexity of the disease and the remedy, varying with the patient."[23] Among the medical fantasies of Dr. Pascal, there is one which confusedly echoes the passages on organic equilibrium that Zola had quoted from Bernard in his essay "Le Roman expérimental." It is Dr. Pascal's last "theory" which he sketched out in his mind before his death:

> Man bathed in a medium, nature which stimulated by
> contact the sensitive terminations of the nerves. Hence
> the impulse given, not only to the senses, but to all the

surfaces of the body, external and internal . . . . what if
the balance were broken . . . he dreamed of a whole
new medication. . . . He saw the world saved again in
this perfect equilibrium, the same quantity of work produced as of sensations received . . . .[24]

Of course this fancied balance of intake and output is only a
blurred reflection of Bernard's concept of equilibrium. One element of Dr. Pascal's therapeutic system comes not from Bernard
but from Brown-Séquard. The injections invented by Dr. Pascal
are like those which Brown-Séquard was said to be administering
to Alphonse Daudet, if not to Zola himself.[25]

The figure of the scientist, once exemplified by Claude Bernard, will continue to receive Zola's admiration during his subsequent career. But when we come to the volume entitled *Paris*
of the trilogy *Les Trois Villes,* it is no longer Bernard but a
living contemporary of Zola's, the chemist Marcellin Berthelot,
who models for his new hero of science, Bertheroy. And soon
Zola will be absorbed in his epic battle in the Dreyfus Case. The
story of his connection with Claude Bernard is definitely over.

It may be an anticlimax to pass from Zola to Paul Bourget.
One may disregard his light society novels and his *Physiologie de
l'amour moderne* on the grounds that they are as irrelevant to our
purpose as Balzac's *Physiologie du mariage.* But as a writer who
came close to adopting medicine as a career, who was always
interested in science, and whose *Le Disciple* (1889) is a milestone in the retreat from positivism, Bourget cannot be overlooked. Maurice Barrès, his fellow-traveler from dilettantism to
conservatism, said of him that "his" book was the *Introduction
to Experimental Medicine.*[26] In the famous novel, the disciple
Robert Greslou compares his inept "psychological investigations"
to the researches of Claude Bernard or Pasteur.[27] But in point of
fact, little if anything of Bernard went into the making of
Greslou's master, the synthetic polymath Adrien Sixte. Sixte is
like Immanuel Kant in his behavior: his neighbors set their
watches by his movements. He is a little like Auguste Comte in
his positivism, like Théodule Ribot in his psychological views.
He is like Hippolyte Taine in his deterministic philosophy and

in his mode of operation, which consists in speculation nourished by the study of documents. Bernard, unlike Taine, could not have imagined that Bourget was aiming at him in this portrait of a closet philosopher. And besides, there is something in a name: Claude Bernard's does not form an anapestic foot, like the others mentioned.

The impact of Bernard is found elsewhere, in various characters of other novels as well as in the system of social conservatism which Bourget tried to graft on some of the newer biological theories. The surgeon Michel Ortègue of *The Sense of Death (Le Sens de la mort)* (1916) is a self-styled follower of the empiricist Magendie. He weds a daughter of a favorite pupil of Claude Bernard, and is fond of quoting both of the famous scientists.[28] The Georges Muller of *Our Actions Follow Us (Nos Actes nous suivent)* (1927) is also a disciple of sorts. A retired chemist from Chicago, he had settled in Cambridge to end his days in study. Upon his death his son discovers that his bedside book is a well-thumbed copy of the *Introduction to Experimental Medicine.* The marginal comments reveal that he had used Bernard's analysis of observation and experiment as a springboard to spiritualism. The spiritual too was a fact that had to be admitted! If the connection with Bernard's book seems farfetched, we are to remember that Cambridge was the home of William James, and it was in the gospel of the Will to Believe that Muller found the answer to determinism.[29]

It transpires that Muller's spiritual travail is the long-deferred effect of a secret crime. His son Patrick discovers in France the evidence that his father had played an unsavory role in the Paris Commune, and had fled to America. There under a false name he had made his fortune. The son mingles in Paris with revolutionists whose ties go back thirty or forty years to the very Communards his father had known. And Patrick falls in love with Marie-Jeanne, daughter of the man his father had betrayed. *Nos actes nous suivent!* This imbroglio is of little significance for us, but it turns out that more than one of the persons frequented by Patrick had studied under Bernard. The socialist Edouard Péreuse had heard with his own ears Bernard making his oft-quoted remark that the frog is the Job of physiology.[30] Another character, Dr. Courrioles, is the *raisonneur* of Bourget's thesis novel. He sets forth one of its lessons: "In psychology as in physiology, the truth lies in the words which the dying Pasteur said to Professor Rénon, who was sitting at his bedside: 'Bernard was right. The germ is nothing. The medium is everything.' "[31] Patrick applies this thesis to the case of Marie-Jeanne, whose misfortunes are too complicated to be related here: "How well Pasteur's expression fits the unhappy girl! The theories of the two Péreuses, there is the seed. Her heredity, that's the soil."[32]

Bourget himself applies such formulae to social problems, often in a doctrinaire and mechanical way. Ever ready to denounce the "scientism" of his opponents, he never hesitates to call upon science to support his own political and social beliefs. More like Cuvier than Bernard in this respect, he sometimes compares society to an organism whose life would be endangered by experimental tinkering. In his *Études et portraits* he argues that the fixity of heredity and the constancy of the vital milieu have their counterpart in society.[33] The reader easily recognizes the Bernardian concept given currency in a distorted form by Bourget's friend Quinton. A similar use of scientific analogy occurs in *Pages de critique* where tradition is equated with the constancy principle, and progress with the law of evolution.[34] Quinton had given an anti-Darwinian twist to the notion of the fixity of the vital milieu, and thus prepared the way for a conservative political application which would have been more difficult with Bernard's original conception. It seems obvious that we are here in the realm of catchwords and specious analogies from which we can expect little genuine elucidation of social and political problems.

In with the large amount of shoddy that swells the literary output of Paul Bourget, there are a few strong novels, some skillful short stories, and a sizeable stock of keen, in fact brilliant critical passages. It must be admitted that neither *Nos Actes nous suivent* nor the essays just mentioned belong in this select category. Perhaps Bourget's respectful attitude toward Bernard can be recorded as amends for the windy attack of a Léon Daudet.

It is customary to deride Zola for his uncritical and misinformed appropriation of Bernard. One hears less mockery of the equally one-sided adaptation made by Zola's opposite numbers. Regardless of Bernard's political conservatism, and in spite of Zola's errors, was he not a truer disciple of the scientific optimism so vigorously voiced by Bernard? Only Zola could have unreservedly indorsed such a declaration as this: "The active role of the experimental sciences does not stop with physics, chemistry, and physiology: it extends into the historical and moral sciences. The modern mind wants to dominate good and evil, to engender and develop the one, to struggle against the other so as to uproot it and wipe it out." Zola's questionable theory of the experimental novel has obscured the fact that, better than many others, he understood the historical importance of Claude Bernard.

CHAPTER Seven

Some Last Things

ATTEMPTING to place Claude Bernard in the history of ideas, we have traced his relation to tradition, his reception by his own age, and his significance for later periods. We have found his imprint in a variety of fields, and have noted how his role has changed with the course of time. Some of his accomplishments have merged with the past and have only a historical importance. Others have assumed with the evolution of modern thought a significance that was at first unrealized. The concept of the inner milieu is the most noteworthy element of a still vital heritage, while his struggle against the animism of Cuvier and Bichat belongs now to history. His influence has been varied, but it has not always been deep. Many readers were content to gather from his store what served their special purposes, while neglecting the rest. Thus our survey inevitably leaves a

129

somewhat miscellaneous if not contradictory impression, for we have had to range hurriedly over a dispersed intellectual landscape.

Let us look backward over the main contours. From the point of view of literature, Bernard can be likened to a distant eminence, rarely explored since Zola and Bourget, and no longer used by novelists taking their literary bearings. Occasionally a Georges Duhamel, a Jules Romains, or an André Gide will cast an upward glance in his direction.[1] In the broad perspective of the history of biology, there are three features that still stand out: the directive idea of life, the conflict with bacteriology, and the concept of the inner environment. It is the first which has been most misunderstood. Depending on one's point of view, Bernard has received the credit or borne the blame for a notion which had been commonly accepted by earlier physiologists, such as Johannes Müller.[2] Bernard adopted it as a convenient if misleading phrase to denote that distinguishing characteristic of living things which cannot be derived from physicochemical laws. The phrase seemed to sanction neo-vitalist interpretations. Bernard, however, never offered it as a final answer, nor did he use it as an excuse to limit research into vital phenomena from the side of physics and chemistry. What argument could be more telling against the vitalists' pre-emption of Bernard than the admission of Bergson, himself a vitalist? Bergson acknowledged that the *idea* was not a force but an explanatory principle, and that Bernard never aimed at giving us a metaphysics of life.[3]

Yet perhaps Bernard's comparative silence on evolution did encourage by default the creative evolution of Bergson. This could have been a result of a gnomic pronouncement like the following:

> The only vital force which we could admit would be a sort of *legislative* force, in no sense executive. To summarize our thought, we could say metaphorically: the vital aim directs phenomena which it does not produce; the physical agents produce phenomena which they do not direct.[4]

The Bergsonian Georges Sorel might well think that this gap in Bernard's thought opened the way for a return of mysticism and

irrationalism into biology. But Bernard was only reserving judgment pending clarification of the issue by the still immature
science of heredity. This is indicated in the very passages cited
by Sorel.[5] The final resolution of the conflict between vitalism
and mechanism has not been, if it ever will be, achieved. The
notion of complementarity applied by Niels Bohr to this question emphasizes anew the persistence of the debate, while perhaps
foreshadowing a dialectical formulation which may help to clear
away the pseudo problems incrusting the subject.[6] In his own
fashion, Bernard was groping toward such a clarification, while
still hampered by Cartesian dualism as well as traces of German
idealism.[7]

Another controversy involving Bernard has been brought to
a close. It is the conflict between physiology and bacteriology
which in an early phase provoked Charles Peirce into calling
Bernard a brake on scientific progress, and later showed Cyon
desperately resisting the triumphant march of the Pasteurians.
The story would be incomplete without the name of Virchow
who was certainly more outspoken than Bernard in his criticism
of bacteriology.[8] Their insistence on the importance of the soil
might seem as one-sided as Pasteur's emphasis on the seed. Yet
even the latter has been quoted, during his last illness, as admitting: "Claude Bernard was right, the germ is nothing, the soil is
everything." Certainly the bacteriologist was not abdicating, for
the successes of his science were incontestable. It was more a
personal remark, a little wry and whimsical, expressing acceptance of the inexorable law of death. Actually both were right in
what they affirmed, wrong in what they denied.[9] In the synthesis
of the two sciences which the future was to bring about, physiology is in one sense perhaps more fundamental, but it must be
coordinated with bacteriology.

The dominance of bacteriology around 1900 was historically
necessary for medical progress.[10] But it did tend to obscure the
significance of Bernard's teachings on the *milieu intérieur*. This
was the very core of physiology as he understood it. It was here
that the crucial experiments had to be made if the science was
to advance. General physiology only came into its inheritance

when further development of the auxiliary sciences made it possible for physiologists such as Pavlov, Henderson, Haldane, and Cannon to carry further Bernard's pioneering work on the self-regulating functions of higher organisms. Moreover, the conceptual pattern here involved could be applied in other sciences. Latent in this conception of self-regulation was the notion of feedback basic to cybernetics. The idea of the inner environment, therefore, must be regarded as something like a *leitmotif* in modern science, and not merely a historical milestone.

What about the philosophical implications of his endeavor? His analysis of method and his emphasis on the need for hypothesis in science no longer have the air of novelty they bore in Second Empire France. Modern philosophy of science has its own problems, raised by theoretical physics, which his rationale of experiment is not adapted to handle. As for the charge that his definition of observation is unsophisticated, one could reply that he prepared the way for a more refined understanding of observational data without going so far as to refine these data almost out of existence.

His general philosophical position may seem from this distance to merge with the agnosticism of Spencer with his Unknowable, of DuBois-Reymond with his *Ignorabimus*. A historian of philosophy, Weber, associates him with the latter, along with Helmholtz, Virchow, Wundt, Taine, and Renan, as exponents of what he calls "positivisme des savants." This is a trend freed from the particular ideas of Comte and the Neo-Criticism of Renouvier.[11] A specialist in French thought, Benrubi, locates him more exactly in the current of criticism of science with Cournot and followed by Poincaré and Duhem. Benrubi, however, unduly emphasizes Bernard as a source for Bergson's vitalism, while omitting a more genuine link with the instrumentalism of this philosopher.[12] Though Bernard stops short of pragmatism, his analogy between theories and tools distinguishes him most radically from his positivist contemporaries. On the other hand, many of his statements show him more optimistic than DuBois-Reymond on the prospects for advances in science. In the closing pages of his *Introduction to Experimental Medicine*, he refuses, unlike DuBois-Reymond, to set a limit to progress in knowledge. It is, to be sure, more characteristic of Bernard to declare that man here below can learn only relative truths and proximate causes.

Yet by a kind of paradox, such relative truths can equip man to become master of the world. This practical note, ringing out so plainly in Bernard's writings, heralds the pragmatist and other activist trends which have, at least until lately, been so conspicuous in our century. But can we miss the echo of a much earlier time when Bacon was proclaiming that knowledge is power and when Descartes himself was proposing a philosophy which through knowledge of natural forces would make us masters and owners of nature? This coincidence with the leader of rationalism gives the clue to the difference between Bernard and pragmatism. Theories are like instruments and must be changed when they become dulled. But the knowledge they yield, though relative and approximate, is more than a recipe for practice. Science is power, and also something more.

Bernard never despaired of the rational explanation of reality. Undaunted by the inexhaustibility, even the apparent absurdity of nature, he was sustained by a robust confidence in the genuine, if slow and painful, march of science. He sensed the grandeur of this struggle against the unknown: "A theory that is displaced dies on the field of honor: it has called forth new facts which have given it a mortal blow, but which have enabled science to advance."[13] He was supported by faith in determinism, but this was for him less a system than it was an explanatory principle. He was in this sense closer to Leonardo da Vinci than to Spinoza or Taine.[14] His aim was to determine the conditions under which phenomena occurred, not to erect a monolithic structure of cause and effect. Science is a going process, a progressive conquest of the indeterminate. Thus there was for him no contradiction in essence between determinism and freedom. Determinism is a necessary condition for freedom of choice. Choices themselves are natural facts, but once made there is no returning. Here was a philosophical question he hoped to clarify, but apparently his time ran out before he could give it the full statement he had in mind. As a result, one of his most promising insights into philosophy never made the impression upon his readers which it deserved to make. Those who would follow this line of approach to the problem of free will are beholden to him for one flash of illumination: "The stability of the inner environment is the condition necessary for a free life."[15]

The cure of disease, the mastery of nature, the quest for knowledge—these held for him something of the value that believers find in religious faith. Did he feel the need of any other? Was Flaubert referring to anything else in his description of Bernard's funeral rites? "The passing of a man like Claude Bernard is a more serious matter than that of an old nobleman like Pius IX. The crowd felt that clearly at Bernard's funeral. I was there. It was religious and very beautiful."[16] Much ink has flowed on the question of Bernard's religious attitude, and many have argued that he ended a believer. Yet the Catholic Sophie O'Brien, daughter of Mme Raffalovich, asserts that he underwent no deathbed conversion.[17] As a Dominican Father wrote: "The statue is beautiful, but the halo is lacking." This was Père Didon, who talked much with Claude Bernard during the last days. Didon quotes Bernard's solicitude for the faith of others: "Father, how grieved I should have been if my science had in any way been able to disturb or combat your faith."[18]

A present-day reader who remembers this wording of Didon's reprint is surprised to see the phrase *"your* faith" given by some commentators as *"our* faith."[19] Is it on such shaky foundations that the argument for Bernard's conversion must rest? Other documents have been produced going back earlier in Bernard's life. One example is the following notation from *Le Cahier rouge:* "Everything disposes me to believe in a higher intelligence, but I cannot have material proof of it; that all remains in the state of faith, of feeling, of certainty nevertheless, and that's what makes me happy." One cannot deny that this may voice Bernard's feelings, but it could be a quotation from the scientist Bienaymé, whose name Bernard wrote in parentheses at the end.[20] A more typical expression of his attitude would seem to be the following: "The scientist thinks of the far-off land, but he works in the present, he goes forward and says: As for the destination (there is one; is it faith? I do not know), when we get to the village, we'll see the houses."[21] It is perhaps this spirit of "Wait and see!" which explains the cryptic remark: "The idea of the immortality of the soul is an experimental idea."[22] According to Sophie O'Brien, he once gladdened her heart with his reasons for believing in immortality.[23] Bernard doubtless experienced moods when he was disposed to believe. On the other hand, he evidently felt a strong reluctance to disturb believing souls with his own doubts.[24] One can find among his papers passages of a distinctly agnostic character. A good example is the leaflet entitled "Notes de Claude Bernard sur la philosophie du doute." Here we may read:

> I put up with ignorance. That is my philosophy . . . . Others cannot live without faith, belief, theory. I do without . . . . I don't know and never will know. I accept it without tormenting myself, I wait—but I do not for all that fall into nihilism—I strive to learn the relations of things.[25]

The attribution of marked religious feelings to Bernard by Jacques Chevalier and Dr. Mauriac has been contested by Dr. Delhoume. This medical scholar's thorough familiarity with the private papers as well as the published canon confers upon his verdict an unequaled authority. He points out how hazardous it is to base one's conclusions on some scattered remarks put on paper more as tentative hypotheses than as peremptory affirmations.[26] It is not a few fragments drawn from his writings by the magnet of personal preference, but only the whole body of his work which can provide an adequate foundation for a definitive judgment.

Fortunately the constant recurrence of certain basic themes enables us to avoid being lost in the detail or confused by the diversity of his production. These basic themes are those we have called the three key ideas: the relation between theory and experiment, the nature of life, and the problem of determinism. Bernard's approach to these questions can be characterized by one term: experimental rationalism.[27] It is as aspects of this central position, never finally stated but ever returned to, that one can best understand the various partial interpretations made of his philosophy from the different directions of relativism, pragmatism, or realism, to mention only a few.

Above all, and worth recalling in our own time, there is the lesson of his confidence in science, in reason and experiment. This was not the bland self-assurance of "scientism," lulled by a naïve belief in the simplicity of the world. He was conscious of but seldom dismayed by the complexity of Nature's web. Faced with the intricacy of reality, the investigator may sometimes feel like Sisyphus, doomed to invariable defeat. *The Education of Henry Adams* presents a well-known expression of this mood of bewilderment before "Twentieth-Century multiplicity." Instead of becoming simpler as it proceeded, science appeared to be becoming ever more unpredictable.[28] Bernard, however, repudiates the fable of Sisyphus: "Néanmoins nous poursuivons toujours nos recherches. La nature est inépuisable, et en cherchant à savoir de plus en plus, nous poursuivons l'évolution de notre nature." ("Nevertheless we continue to pursue our researches. Nature is inexhaustible, and in seeking to learn more and more we pursue the development of our own nature.") With the aid of science, mankind becomes a veritable "contremaître de la création."[29] Bernard's stubborn confidence in man's powers could still serve as one remedy against failure of nerve.

NOTES

(The translation of all quotations is the author's
unless it is explicitly stated otherwise.)

INTRODUCTION

1. Edmond and Jules de Goncourt, *Journal, Mémoires de la vie littéraire* (Académie Goncourt edition, Monaco, 1956), XVII, pp. 18-19.

2. Anatole de Monzie, *Les Veuves abusives* (Paris, 1936), pp. 85-100.

3. J. M. D. and E. Harris Olmsted, *Claude Bernard and the Experimental Method in Medicine* (New York: Henry Schuman, 1952), p. 154.

4. Olmsted, p. 252.

5. Goncourt, *Journal*, VIII, pp. 192-193.

6. Paul Bert, "Les Travaux de Claude Bernard," in *L'Œuvre de Claude Bernard* (Paris, 1881), p. 86; Louis Pasteur, "Claude Bernard," *Le Moniteur universel*, Nov. 7, 1866, reprinted in *Œuvres de Pasteur* (Paris, 1922), II, p. 493.

CHAPTER ONE

1. Olmsted, p. 10; Ernest Renan, "Claude Bernard," in *L'Œuvre de Claude Bernard*, p. 17.

2. Claude Bernard, *Arthur de Bretagne*, ed. J. M. Le Goff, 2nd ed. (Paris, 1943).

3. Renan, pp. 22-23.

4. Bert, p. 51.

5. Dr. E. Chauffard, "Claude Bernard," *Revue des Deux-Mondes*, XXX (Nov. 15, 1878), 283. This review will be abbreviated *RDM*.

6. Bernard, *La Science expérimentale*, 6th ed. (Paris, 1918), p. 309.

7. Renan, p. 25.

8. Bernard, *Principes de médecine expérimentale*, ed. Delhoume (Paris: Presses Universitaires de France, 1947), pp. 259-261. This book will be abbreviated *Principes*, without name of author.

9. Goncourt, *Journal*, VIII, p. 200.

10. Dr. Léon Delhoume, *De Claude Bernard à d'Arsonval* (Paris: J. B. Baillière fils, 1939), pp. 37-57.

11. *La Science expérimentale*, pp. 434-440.

12. Bernard, *Leçons de pathologie expérimentale*, 2nd ed. (Paris, 1880); *Leçons sur les phénomènes de la vie communs aux animaux et aux végétaux* (Paris, 1878-1879), 2 vol. Henceforth abbreviated *Phénomènes*.

13. Renan, p. 28; Ferdinand Brunetière, "Discours sur Claude Bernard," in *Institut de France* (Paris, 1894), p. 7; Henri Bergson, "La Philosophie de Claude Bernard," in *La Pensée et le mouvant*, 12th ed. (Paris: Presses Universitaires de France, 1941), p. 229.

14. Dr. Pierre Mauriac, *Claude Bernard* (Paris: Grasset, 1954), pp. 108-110. The school editions of Part One are edited by Maurice Dorolle, Nouvelle éd. refondue (Paris: Lib. Delagrave, 1954), and by Marc Soriano (Paris: Classiques Larousse, 1951).

15. I. Bernard Cohen, Foreword of Dover ed. of Claude Bernard, *An Introduction to the Study of Experimental Medicine* (New York: Macmillan, 1957). See also George Schwartz and Philip W. Bishop, *Moments of Discovery* (New York, 1958), I, pp. 61-71; II, pp. 622-630.

16. Bernard, *Introduction à l'étude de la médecine expérimentale* (Paris: Flammarion, 1952), p. 40. This book will be abbreviated IEME without name of author.

17. IEME, p. 58.

18. *Principes*, p. xxvi.

19. Bert, p. 79.

20. IEME, pp. 65, 66.

21. IEME, p. 70.

22. IEME, p. 72.

23. André Lalande, *Vocabulaire technique et critique de la philosophie* (Paris: Presses Universitaires de France, 1947), p. 196.

24. IEME, p. 80.

25. IEME, p. 90.

26. IEME, p. 95.

27. Hippolyte Taine, *Les Philosophes classiques du XIXe siècle*, 10th ed. (Paris, 1910), p. 324.

28. C.-A. Sainte-Beuve, *Premiers Lundis*, 2 me éd. (Paris, 1879), III, p. 308.

29. IEME, pp. 103-107.

30. IEME, pp. 111, 128.

31. IEME, pp. 112-117.

32. IEME, p. 150, cf. Georges Canguilhem, *La Connaissance de la vie* (Paris, 1952), p. 40.

33. IEME, p. 182.

34. IEME, p. 189.

35. J. R. Kantor, *The Logic of Modern Science* (Bloomington, Ind.: Principia Press, 1953), p. 129.

36. IEME, pp. 194-195.

37. IEME, p. 295.

38. *La Science expérimentale*, p. 428.

39. *Ibid.*, pp. 367-403.

40. Bernard, *Le Cahier rouge* (Paris: NRF, 1942). Dr. Mauriac, *op. cit.*, pp. 209-228.

41. Bernard, *Lettres beaujolaises*, ed. Justin Godart (Villefranche-sur-Saône: Éditions du Cuvier, 1950), p. 177. The Chevreul story is from Marcellin Berthelot, *Science et libre pensée* (Paris, 1905), p. 253.

42. *Principes*, p. xiii.

43. Cf. *Principes*, p. 210 and IEME, p. 91.

44. *Principes*, p. 173 and IEME, p. 294.

45. Bernard, *Pensées. Notes détachées*, ed. Delhoume (Paris: J. B. Baillière fils, 1937), pp. 27-90. This title will be abbreviated *Pensées* without name of author.

46. Bernard, *Philosophie, manuscrit inédit*, ed. Jacques Chevalier (Paris: Boivin, 1937). This title will be abbreviated *Philosophie* without name of author.
47. *Philosophie*, p. 12.
48. *Ibid.*, p. 19.
49. *Ibid.*, p. 24.
50. *Ibid.*, p. 26.
51. *Ibid.*, p. 29.
52. *Principes*, p. 206.

CHAPTER TWO

1. *Philosophie*, p. 12.
2. *Pensées*, p. 44.
3. *Pensées*, p. 56.
4. Cf. *Principes*, p. xxviii.
5. *Pensées*, p. 64.
6. *La Science expérimentale*, p. 212.
7. Carton CXII, non classé, Archives Claude Bernard, Collège de France.
8. *Philosophie*, p. 18.
9. *Pensées*, p. 29.
10. *Pensées*, p. 82.
11. Cf. *La Science expérimentale*, p. 369.
12. *Principes*, p. 210.
13. Ferdinand Brunetière, *Discours de combat* (Paris, 1912), III, p. 243.
14. IEME, p. 91.
15. IEME, p. 91.
16. IEME, pp. 91-92.
17. *Principes*, p. 126, also pp. 137, 211.
18. *Philosophie*, p. 37.
19. *Leçons de pathologie expérimentale*, p. 481.
20. *Lettres beaujolaises*, pp. 77, 85.
21. IEME, p. 79. Cf. *Principes*, p. xxxviii.
22. IEME, pp. 93-95.
23. IEME, p. 135.
24. *La Science expérimentale*, p. 211.
25. *Ibid.*, pp. 151-152.
26. *Philosophie*, p. 19.
27. The references here are to the English translation of Johnson: Tennemann, *A Manual of the History of Philosophy* (London, 1870), p. 343.
28. *Philosophie*, p. 19.
29. *Pensées*, p. 69.
30. Lalande, *op. cit.*, p. 214.
31. *Principes*, p. 207.

32. IEME, p. 53.

33. Pascal, *Pensées et opuscules*, ed. Brunschvicg (Paris, 1953), p. 78.

34. Cahiers, no. 3, Archives Claude Bernard, Collège de France. Cf. *Philosophie*, p. 19.

35. IEME, p. 76; cf. *Principes*, p. 219.

36. Pascal, p. 560.

37. *La Science expérimentale*, p. 201; Pascal, p. 168.

38. Registre, Carton CXII, Archives Claude Bernard, Collège de France. Cf. *Phénomènes*, I, pp. 22-24.

39. IEME, p. 294; cf. Pascal, p. 389.

40. *Principes*, p. 173; *Philosophie*, p. 42.

41. *Principes*, p. 173.

42. *Principes*, pp. 107, 136, 172, notes; *Phénomènes*, I, p. 204.

43. Georges Barral, 'Diderot et la médecine, un Ouvrage projeté par Claude Bernard," *La Chronique médicale*, Feb. 15, 1900, 126-128.

44. IEME, p. 47; *Leçons de pathologie expérimentale*, p. 515.

45. *Philosophie*, p. 22; *Le Cahier rouge*, p. 151.

46. Henry D. Aiken, *The Age of Ideology* (New York, 1956) p. 30.

47. IEME, pp. 109, 127.

48. Abel Rey, *Les Sciences philosophiques, leur état actuel* (Paris, 1908), pp. 616-617; Kant, *Critique of Judgment*, II, sec. 65, 66, 72; *La Science expérimentale*, p. 211; *Phénomènes*, I, p. 338.

49. *Philosophie*, p. 37. But cf. *Lettres beaujolaises*, p. 94.

50. *Le Cahier rouge*, pp. 117-118.

51. *Philosophie*, p. 23.

52. *Principes*, pp. 61, 136, 171, 208.

53. Tennemann, p. 455.

54. *Philosophie*, p. 24.

55. IEME, pp. 47, 69.

56. IEME, p. 138.

57. *Principes*, p. 142.

58. *Principes*, p. 231.

59. *Phénomènes*, I, p. 332. Cyon's reference is to a conversation in 1866. Elie de Cyon, *Les Nerfs du cœur, anatomie et physiologie* (Paris, 1905). p. 109, note 1.

60. "If they reproach me with not being philosophical, it is because I know the falsity of these views from the practical point of view." *Principes*, p. 231. Also p. 143.

61. Émile Bréhier, *Histoire de la philosophie* (Paris, 1932), II, II, p. 1002.

62. Olmsted, p. 142.

63. Paul Janet, *Les Causes finales*, 2nd ed. (Paris, 1882), pp. 43, 70, 104, 163-183, 319.

64. *Phénomènes*, I, pp. 335-336. Bernard refers to the 1876 edition of Janet.

65. *Phénomènes*, I, pp. 337-339, 341.

66. Janet, "Le Matérialisme contemporain," *RDM* (Aug. 15, 1863), XLVI, 886.

67. *Principes*, p. 243.

68. Carton CXII, Pièces non classées, Archives Claude Bernard, Collège de France.

69. Hermann Lotze, *Microcosmos*, trans. Hamilton and Jones (New York, 1885), I, p. 125.

70. Dr. Mauriac, p. 19.

71. Rabelais, p. 218; La Fontaine, pp. 70, 84; Fontenelle, p. 57 (mistaken by Delhoume; see his note), *Principes*. Boileau, p. 39; La Mennais, p. 45, *Pensées*. Rousseau, pp. 13, 22, *Lettres beaujolaises*. Musset, p. 40, *Philosophie*. On Montaigne, esp. the unpub. "Note de Claude Bernard sur la philosophie du doute," Archives Claude Bernard.

72. *Lettres beaujolaises*, pp. 11, 17, 21, 98, 184, 200; Dr. Georges Morin, *Sainte-Beuve et la médecine* (Paris, 1928), pp. 173-174.

73. Lalande, *Les Théories de l'induction et de l'expérimentation* (Paris: Boivin, 1929), p. 201.

CHAPTER THREE

1. Dr. Mauriac, pp. 152 f.; C. Hillimand, "Auguste Comte et Claude Bernard," *La Revue Positiviste internationale* ("18 Homère 126," i.e., Feb. 15, 1914), XIV, 169; Louis André-Nuytz, "Le Spiritualisme et l'école expérimentale," *La Philosophie positive*, Revue dirigée par Littré (Jan.-Feb. 1869), IV, 148.

2. Taine, pp. ix-x. Cf. D. D. Rosca, *L'Influence de Hegel sur Taine* (Paris, 1928), p. 248; Lalande, *Vocabulaire technique*, p. 774.

3. *Philosophie*, p. 35.

4. *Lettres beaujolaises*, p. 180.

5. *Principes*, p. 247.

6. *Principes*, p. 84.

7. IEME, p. 125. Bernard's immediate source was apparently Vacherot. See *Pensées*, p. 85.

8. *Philosophie*, p. 28.

9. *Philosophie*, p. 37.

10. IEME, pp. 296-297.

11. IEME, p. 65.

12. *Principes*, pp. 1-3, 36-58, 76-81. For Comte's forerunners Turgot, Cuvier and St. Simon, cf. George Boas, *French Philosophies of the Romantic Period* (Baltimore, 1925), p. 263.

13. Auguste Comte, *Cours de philosophie positive*, 5th ed. (Paris, 1895), I, p. 23; Bernard, *Principes*, p. 135.

14. Comte, pp. 24-25.

15. *Philosophie*, p. 35.

16. IEME, p. 50.

17. IEME, p. 62.

18. IEME, p. 63.

19. Comte, III, p. 220.

20. Comte, III, pp. 220-221.

21. *Principes,* pp. 302 and 247.

22. Comte, III, p. 224.

23. Registre, Carton CXII, Archives Claude Bernard, MS p. 235.

24. IEME, p. 293.

25. IEME, p. 295.

26. Bréhier, pp. 869, 879-880.

27. Comte, III, p. 251.

28. Comte, III, pp. 255, 258-259, 263, 265.

29. Thomas Henry Huxley, *Science and Education* (New York, 1896), pp. 49 f.

30. IEME, pp. 56-57. Cf. Comte, III, p. 266; also IEME, p. 268, *Principes,* p. 247.

31. IEME, p. 179.

32. Comte, III, p. 239.

33. *Ibid.,* pp. 326, 327-328.

34. IEME, p. 183.

35. IEME, p. 195.

36. IEME, pp. 101-102, 179, 265.

37. *Philosophie,* p. 29.

38. Maurice Caullery, *La Science française depuis le XVIIIe siècle* (Paris: Armand Colin, 1948), 2nd ed., pp. 146-147. Cf. also Caullery, "La Nature des lois biologiques," *Revue de métaphysique et de morale* (1914), XXII, 334-338. This review will be abbreviated RMM.

39. IEME, p. 33.

40. IEME, pp. 54, 90, 120-121, 128, 196, 200. Cf. Descartes, *Discours de la méthode,* 6me partie, cited by Bernard in *Phénomènes,* I, p. 377.

41. Paul Janet, "La Méthode expérimentale et la physiologie," *RDM* (April 15, 1866), LXII, 917; E. Caro, *Le Matérialisme et la science* (Paris, 1867), 2nd ed., p. 62. For Comte on hypothesis, see *Cours,* II, pp. 300, 312, 446.

CHAPTER FOUR

1. *Principes,* p. 192.

2. *Pensées,* pp. 42, 44.

3. IEME, p. 70.

4. Caro, pp. 34-36.

5. Ravaisson, *La Philosophie en France au XIXe siècle* (Paris, 1868), p. 121. Cf. R. Lenoir, "Claude Bernard et l'Esprit expérimental," *Revue Philosophique* (1919), LXXXVII, 94: "Using an ambiguous terminology and an interpretation whose superficiality is somewhat surprising, Caro and Ravaisson discover in Claude Bernard an idealist unaware (un spiritualiste sans le savoir)."

6. Lachelier, *Du Fondement de l'induction,* 7th ed. (Paris, 1916), pp. 10-11. Alfred Fouillée disputes Lachelier's argument in *Le Mouvement idealiste et la réaction contre la science positive* (Paris, 1896), p. 137.

7. *Le Cahier rouge,* p. 150.

8. Dr. Mauriac, p. 144. Another writer who regards Bernard as an empiricist is Maurice Delacre, "Wurtz et Claude Bernard," *Mercure de France* (Feb 15, 1922), CLIV, 39-57. But unlike Mauriac, Delacre finds in this alleged empiricism reason for praise. He takes Bernard's *caveat* against systems for a *caveat* against hypotheses!

9. Ravaisson, pp. 247-248.

10. *La Science expérimentale,* pp. 113 f. IEME pp. 140-141.

11. *Phénomènes,* II, p. 51.

12. The idealists include: Janet, p. 930; Caro, p. 47; Renouvier, *Essais de critique générale,* 2me essai, 2nd ed. (Paris, 1875), I, pp. 56-57; A. E. A. Ferrand, *Claude Bernard et la science contemporaine* (Paris, 1879), p. 22; Émile Boutroux, *De l'Idée de loi naturelle* (Paris, 1895), p. 74; Hans Driesch, *Der Vitalismus als Geschichte und als Lehre* (Leipzig, 1905), p. 123; Pierre Lamy, *Claude Bernard et le matérialisme* (Paris, 1929), pp. 24, 64-65; Père Sertillanges, *La Philosophie de Claude Bernard* (Paris, 1943), p. 10.

    On the "materialist" side are Charles Letourneau, *Science et matérialisme* (Paris, 1879), pp. 416-426, first published in *La Pensée nouvelle,* May 10, 1868; Jules Soury, *Le Système nerveux central* (Paris, 1899), II, p. 1772; Jean-Louis Faure, *Claude Bernard* (Paris, 1925), p. 197; Henri Roger, "La Philosophie de Claude Bernard," extrait de la *Presse médicale* (Aug. 7, 21; Sept. 11; Oct. 9, 23, 1935), p. 7.

13. Ravaisson, p. 135. Cf. R. Lenoir's discussion of Ravaisson's misunderstanding of Bernard in "La Doctrine de Ravaisson et la pensée moderne," *RMM* (1919), 397.

14. *La Science expérimentale,* p. 211.

15. *Pensées,* p. 52.

16. *La Pensée nouvelle,* Paris, 1866-1869.

17. Pierre Martino, *Le Naturalisme français,* 2nd ed. (Paris, 1950), pp. 34-42.

18. *La Pensée nouvelle,* June 7, 1868, pp. 26 f.

19. Letourneau, p. 416.

20. Faure, pp. 176-179.

21. Renan, pp. 33-34.

22. Delhoume, *De Claude Bernard à d'Arsonval,* p. 36.

23. Delhoume, p. 36, note 1. Cf. *Le Cahier rouge,* p. 126.

24. Registre CXII, Archives Claude Bernard, MS p. 235.

25. *Ibid.,* p. 239; cf. *Pensées,* pp. 35, 38, 47, 57; and "La Définition de la vie," *La Science expérimentale,* pp. 198-212.

26. Registre CXII, p. 219.

27. *La Science expérimentale,* p. 109.

28. Registre CXII, p. 161.

29. *Ibid.*, p. 150.
30. *La Science expérimentale*, pp. 210-211.
31. Boutroux, p. 74; Lamy, p. 64.
32. Sertillanges, p. 38.
33. Claude Bernard, *Introduction à l'étude de la médecine expérimentale*, publ. avec des notes critiques par le R.-P. Sertillanges (Paris, 1900).
34. Sertillanges, *La Philosophie de Claude Bernard*, p. 68.
35. Cf. IEME, pp. 90 f., *La Science expérimentale*, p. 79.
36. Brunetière, p. 19.
37. Lamy, p. 61.
38. Roger, pp. 7, 10.
39. Roger, pp. 25, 30-31.
40. *Phénomènes*, I, p. 62. Cf. *Principes*, p. 207.
41. Lamy, p. 33.

CHAPTER FIVE

1. W. Riese, "Claude Bernard in the Light of Modern Science," *Bulletin of the History of Medicine*, Johns Hopkins University Press (Oct. 1943), XIV, p. 294.
2. Jacques Loeb, *The Organism as a Whole* (New York, 1916), pp. 2-4.
3. Faure, pp. 153-156, 170.
4. Cf. Yves Delage, *L'Hérédité et les grands problèmes de la biologie générale*, 2nd ed. (Paris, 1903), p. 436; Driesch, p. 123.
5. John F. Fulton, *Physiology* (Clio Medica series, no. 5, New York, 1931), p. 112.
6. Fulton, *Selected Readings in the History of Physiology* (Springfield: C. C. Thomas, Publisher, 1930), pp. 307 f.
7. Sir Michael Foster, *Claude Bernard* (London, 1899), p. 8.
8. Olmsted, p. 224. Cf. also John Theodore Merz, *A History of European Thought in the XIXth Century* (Edinburgh, 1903), II, p. 432.
9. Walter B. Cannon, *The Wisdom of the Body* (New York, Norton, 1939), 2nd ed., p. 21.
10. William James, "Claude Bernard's *Rapport* . . . ," *North American Review* (1868), CVII, p. 324.
11. Cf. Rhoda Truax, *Joseph Lister* (New York, 1944), p. 169.
12. Lewes, *The Physical Basis of Mind*, second series of *Problems of Life and Mind* (Boston, 1877), pp. 172, 225, 227, 234-235.
13. Lewes, pp. 49-50.
14. Renouvier, p. 162.
15. Léon Fredericq, "Influences du milieu ambiant sur la composition du sang des animaux aquatiques," *Archives de zoologie expérimentale et générale* (1885), 2me série, III, xxxiv-xxxviii.
16. René Quinton, *L'Eau de mer milieu organique*, 2nd ed. (Paris, 1912), p. 86, note 1.

17. Cf. Lucien Corpechot, *Souvenirs d'un journaliste* (Paris, 1936), I, pp. 150, 157, 170-210; Paul Bourget, *Pages de critique* (Paris, 1910), II, p. 143; Remy de Gourmont, *Promenades philosophiques*, 2nd series (Paris, 1908), pp. 7 ff.; Jules de Gaultier, *La Dépendance de la morale et l'indépendance des mœurs* (Paris, 1907), pp. 199 ff.; Weber, "Les Théories biologiques de M. René Quinton," *RMM* (1905), XIII, 114-141.

18. Fulton, *Selected Readings* . . . , p. 13.

19. Bernard, *An Introduction to the Study of Experimental Medicine*, pp. viii-ix.

20. J. S. Haldane, *Respiration* (New York, 1922).

21. Henderson, *The Order of Nature, an Essay* (Cambridge, 1917), pp. 77, 110; Haldane, *The Sciences and Philosophy* (New York, 1929), pp. 38-39, 42, 47, 54.

22. Cannon, *La Sagesse du corps* (Paris: Editions de la Nouvelle Revue Critique, 1939), Préface.

23. Cannon, *The Wisdom of the Body*, pp. 37-38, 263.

24. Cannon, p. 38.

25. Sir Charles Sherrington, *Man on His Nature* (New York, 1953), 2nd ed., p. 136.

26. Sir Joseph Barcroft, *Features in the Architecture of Physiological Function* (New York: Macmillan, and Cambridge University Press, 1934), p. 87. Cf. also his *The Brain and Its Environment* (New Haven, 1938), pp. 83 f., and Henry McIlwain, *Chemotherapy and the Central Nervous System* (Boston, 1957), pp. 283-284.

27. Fielding H. Garrison, *An Introduction to the History of Medicine*, 4th ed. (Philadelphia, 1929), p. 695.

28. Garrison, "History of Endocrine Doctrine," in *Endocrinology and Metabolism*, ed. L. F. Barker (New York, 1922), I, pp. 58-60; Georges Dumas, *Traité de psychologie* (Paris, 1924), II, pp. 1071-1073; E. Gley, *Les grands problèmes de l'endocrinologie* (Paris, 1926), pp. 9-18, 29, 62-66.

29. *Les Nerfs du cœur, anatomie et physiologie*, p. 58, note 1.

30. W. Grey Walter, *The Living Brain* (New York, 1953), pp. 35, 70, 137. Norbert Wiener, *I Am a Mathematician* (New York: Doubleday, 1956), p. 291.

31. Norbert Wiener, *Cybernetics* (Cambridge, Mass.: Technology Press, 1948), p. 135.

32. Pierre de Latil, *La Pensée artificielle* (Paris, 1953), pp. 14 f., 54, 107, 293, 298.

33. Hans Selye, *The Stress of Life* (New York: McGraw-Hill, 1956), pp. 27, 47.

34. Selye, pp. 11-12. H. Laborit, *Réaction organique à l'agression et choc* (Paris, 1952), pp. 1-4, 11. René Leriche, *Bases de la chirurgie physiologique* (Paris, 1955), p. 112.

35. Selye, p. 26.

36. Dr. Iago Galdston, *Progress in Medicine* (New York: Alfred A. Knopf, Inc., 1940), pp. 110-112. Leriche, p. 40.

37. Selye, p. 205.

38. Sir William Osler, *The Principles and Practice of Medicine*, 10th ed., revised by McCrae (New York, 1925), p. 160.

39. Cf. Dr. Mauriac, p. 159.

40. Dr. Mauriac, p. 158; also his *Nouvelles Rencontres* (Paris, 1930), p. 174.

41. *Collected Papers of Charles Sanders Peirce*, ed. by Hartshorne and Weiss (Cambridge: Harvard University Press, 1931), I, p. 45.

42. *Leçons de pathologie expérimentale*, p. 17.

43. *Œuvres de Pasteur*, II, p. 486; V, p. 45; VI, p. 15, VII, pp. 11, 427, 433.

44. *Les Nerfs du cœur, anatomie et physiologie*, pp. x-xv, xxxiii.

45. Jean Rostand. *Hommes de vérité* (Paris, 1955), I, pp. 76-79; Dr. Mauriac, *Claude Bernard*, pp. 127-135.

46. Alexis Carrel and Charles A. Lindbergh, *The Culture of Organs* (New York, 1938), pp. 3-4. The book is dedicated to the memory of Claude Bernard.

47. *Pensées*, pp. 339-340.

48. Rostand, p. 78.

49. *Principes*, p. xli.

50. Henry Maudsley, *Body and Will* (New York, 1884), p. 67.

51. Edwin G. Boring, *A History of Experimental Psychology*, 1st ed. (New York, 1929), p. 41, 2nd ed. (New York, 1950), p. 18.

52. Kimball Young, *Personality and Problems of Adjustment*, 2nd ed. (New York, 1952), p. 12; Gardner Murphy, *Personality, a Biosocial Approach to Origins and Structure* (New York, 1947), p. 32; Andras Angyal, *Foundations for a Science of Personality* (New York, 1941), pp. 90 f.

53. Translated from Delhoume's citation, *Principes*, p. xlii.

54. Friedrich Nietzsche, *Der Wille zur Macht, Werke* (Leipzig, 1906) IX, p. 39. Cf. Georges Canguilhem, *Essai sur quelques problèmes concernant le normal et le pathologique* (Paris, 1950), pp. 14-17, 31-55.

55. Ribot, *La Psychologie des sentiments*, 15th edition (Paris: Alcan, Presses Universitaires de France, 1939), p. 63.

56. Ribot, pp. 118-119.

57. Y. P. Frolov, *Pavlov and His School*, trans. Dutt (London, 1937), p. 247; B. P. Babkin, *Pavlov, a Biography* (Chicago: University of Chicago Press, 1949), p. 337.

58. Ivan P. Pavlov, *Experimental Psychology and Other Essays* (New York, 1957), p. 87.

59. Pavlov, p. 36. Cf. *Sämtliche Werke* (Berlin, 1954), I, p. 432.

60. Pavlov, pp. 87 f.

61. Babkin, p. 206.

62. Babkin, p. 219.

63. Harry K. Wells, *Ivan P. Pavlov* (New York: International Publishers, 1956), p. 103.

64. Wells, p. 104.

65. R. H. Shryock, *The Development of Modern Medicine* (Philadelphia, 1936), p. 300.

66. Bergson, "La Philosophie de Claude Bernard," p. 230.

67. *Œuvres de Pasteur*, II, p. 493, article from *Le Moniteur universel*, Nov. 7, 1866.

68. Paul Foulquié, *Claude Bernard* (Paris, 1954), pp. 131-133; Marcel Boll and Jacques Reinhart, "La Logique en France au XXe siècle," in *L'Activité philosophique contemporaine en France et aux États-Unis*, ed. Marvin Farber (Paris, 1950), II, p. 212.

69. Lalande, *Vocabulaire technique* . . . , p. 196.

70. Louis Rougier, *La Structure des Théories Déductives* (Paris, 1921), p. 15; Émile Meyerson, *Du Cheminement de la pensée* (Paris, 1931), I, p. 111; III, p. 844.

71. George H. von Wright, *The Logical Problem of Induction* (Helsinki, 1941), pp. 8, 199.

72. *Pensées*, p. 32.

73. *Pensées*, p. 88.

74. *Principes*, pp. 187, 195; IEME, p. 110.

75. Comte, II, pp. 335-338.

76. Ernest Naville, *La Logique de l'hypothèse*, 2nd ed. (Paris, 1895), pp. 7-13, 27, 250.

77. Federigo Enriques, *Problems of Science*, trans. K. Royce (Chicago: Open Court, 1914), p. 83.

78. Cf. W. Stanley Jevons, *The Principles of Science* (London, 1887), pp. 504-524.

79. Morris R. Cohen and Ernest Nagel, *An Introduction to Logic and Scientific Method* (New York: Harcourt Brace, 1934), p. 200.

80. Meyerson, I, p. 16. Cf. IEME, p. 72.

81. J. R. Kantor, *The Logic of Modern Science*, p. 8; Max Black, "The Definition of Scientific Method," in *Science and Civilization*, ed. Stauffer (Madison: University of Wisconsin Press, 1949), pp. 83-89; Pierre Vendryès, *L'Acquisition de la science* (Paris, 1946), pp. 36-39, 354, 382; R. Taton, *Reason and Chance in Scientific Discovery*, trans. A. J. Pomerans (New York, 1957), pp. 43-44.

82. Kantor, p. 8.

83. Black, pp. 83-84. Cf. IEME, p. 231.

84. Cited by Renouvier, *op. cit.*, 3nd essai (nouvelle édition), p. 105, from Sainte-Claire Deville, *Étude sur la dissociation*.

85. IEME, pp. 79, 97.

86. Black, pp. 88-90.

87. IEME, pp. 76-77; *Principes*, p. 173.

88. Black, p. 89; Bergson, p. 231.

89. Lancelot Hogben, *Statistical Theory* (New York: W. W. Norton, n.d.), pp. 227-229, 341.

90. Pierre Duhem, *La Théorie physique; son objet et sa structure* (Paris, 1906), p. 299.

91. Renan, p. 33.

92. Renan, *Œuvres complètes* (Paris, 1947), I, p. 633.

93. Renan, *L'Avenir de la science*, 3rd ed. (Paris, 1890), p. 259.

94. Renan, *Œuvres complètes* (Paris, 1948), II, p. 852.

95. *Ibid.*, p. 1171, note.

96. Cf. Berthelot, "La Science idéale et la science positive," in Renan, *Œuvres complètes*, I, p. 660.

97. Renan, *L'Avenir de la science*, p. 150.

98. *Philosophie*, p. 27.

99. Renan, *Œuvres complètes*, II, p. 843.

100. Anatole France, *Œuvres complètes illustrées* (Paris: Calmann Lévy, 1927), IX, p. 507.

101. *Ibid.*, p. 409.

102. *Philosophie*, p. 43.

103. Jules de Gaultier, *Le Bovarysme*, nouvelle éd. (Paris, 1921), pp. 50-51.

104. Gaultier, *De Kant à Nietzsche*, 4th ed. (Paris, 1910), pp. 124-127; also *La Fiction universelle* (Paris, 1903), p. 392.

105. Bourquin, "Un Maître à penser universel; Claude Bernard," introd. IEME (Flammarion 1952 ed. used here), p. 10.

106. Remy de Gourmont, *Promenades philosophiques*, 12th ed. (Paris, 1931), p. 166.

107. Gourmont, *Nouvelles Dissociations* (Paris, 1925), p. 186.

108. Gourmont, *Promenades philosophiques*, II, pp. 7-95; 115-123.

109. Gourmont, *Une Nuit au Luxembourg*, 22nd ed. (Paris, 1925), pp. 74 f.

110. Lamy, *L'Introduction à l'étude de la médecine expérimentale, Claude Bernard, le naturalisme et le positivisme* (Paris, 1928), p. 32.

111. P. V. Rubow, *Hippolyte Taine, Étapes de son œuvre* (Paris, 1930), p. 100.

112. *Hippolyte Taine, vie et correspondance* (Paris, 1904), II, p. 41.

113. *Ibid.*, p. 326.

114. Cf. Rosca, p. 248.

115. See Victor Giraud, *Essai sur Taine* (Paris, 1901), p. 84, note.

116. Taine, *De l'Intelligence* (Paris, 1948), II, pp. 454-455.

117. Alexander Bain, *Dissertations on Leading Philosophical Topics* (London, 1903), p. 143.

118. Léon Daudet, *Le stupide XIXe Siècle* (Paris: Grasset, 1924), pp. 145-146.

119. Daudet, p. 163.

120. Félix Le Dantec, *Contre la Métaphysique* (Paris, 1912), p. 51. Cited by I. Benrubi, *Les Sources et les courants de la philosophie contemporaine en France* (Paris, 1933), I, p. 138.

121. Le Dantec, *Eléments de Philosophie biologique* (Paris, 1911), p. 177. Bernard's pupil A. Dastre answers Le Dantec in *Life and Death*, trans. Greenstreet (New York, 1911), *passim*.

122. Le Dantec, *Les Lois naturelles* (Paris, 1904), p. 213.

123. Le Dantec, *Le Conflit, Entretiens philosophiques*, 4th ed. (Paris, 1905), pp. 15-17, 239-240.

124. Georges Sorel, "Les Préoccupations métaphysiques des physiciens contemporains," *RMM* (Nov. 1905), XIII, 874-875, 877, 880. Cf. also his "Vues sur les problèmes de la philosophie," *RMM* (Sept. 1910), XVIII, 589, 592.

125. Henri Poincaré, *La Science et l'hypothèse* (Paris, 1902), p. 90; *La Valeur de la Science* (Paris, 1905), p. 142.

126. Bergson, pp. 230-236.

127. Bergson, p. 237.

128. Bergson, *L'Évolution créatrice*, 6th ed. (Paris, 1910), p. 135.

129. *L'Évolution créatrice*, p. 273.

130. IEME, p. 121.

131. Bergson, "La Philosophie de Claude Bernard," p. 235.

132. *Lettres beaujolaises*, pp. 107-108.

133. *La Science expérimentale*, p. 133.

134. Samuel Butler, *Unconscious Memory* (London, 1924), pp. 13-27. See C. E. M. Joad, *Samuel Butler* (London, 1924), p. 35.

135. *Lettres beaujolaises*, p. 109.

136. Cf. René Berthelot, *Un Romantisme utilitaire, étude sur le mouvement pragmatiste* (Paris, 1913), II, pp. 101-111.

137. Bergson, "La Philosophie," in *La Science française* (Paris, 1915), p. 12.

138. Julien Benda, "À propos de la 'philosophie française,'" *Mercure de France* (Sept. 9, 1915), CXII, p. 186.

139. Benda, "Réponse aux défenseurs du bergsonisme," *Mercure de France* (June 16, 1913), CIV, 302.

140. Benda, *De Quelques Constantes de l'esprit humain* (Paris: Gallimard, 1950), p. 151.

141. William James, *Pragmatism, a New Name for Some Old Ways of Thinking* (New York: Longmans, Green, 1948), pp. 53-54.

142. Paul Lafargue, *Critiques littéraires* (Paris, 1936), p. 178.

143. Lucy Prenant, "Marx et Comte," in *À la Lumière du Marxisme*, tome II (Paris, 1937), p. 71.

144. See the introduction and notes to the edition of Soriano. Also the Claude Bernard issue of *Les Cahiers rationalistes* (no. 144, Jan.-Feb. 1955), with contributions by Dr. André Bourguignon, "La Pensée de Claude Bernard," and Dr. G.-Cl. Velley, "Les Répercussions de l'œuvre de Claude Bernard."

145. René Berthelot, *Un Romantisme utilitaire. Le Pragmatisme chez Nietzsche et chez Poincaré* (Paris, 1911), I, pp. 101-102, 293-294.

146. R. Lenoir, "Claude Bernard et l'Esprit expérimental," pp. 94-95.

147. *La Science expérimentale*, p. 109.

CHAPTER SIX

1. Sully Prudhomme, *Œuvres* (Paris: Alphonse Lemerre, 1887), IV, pp. 265-266.

2. C. A. Sainte-Beuve, *Causeries du Lundi*, 3rd ed. (Paris, n.d.), XIII, p. 364.

3. Feodor Dostoyevsky, *The Brothers Karamazov*, trans. Garnett (New York, 1915), pp. 634, 644, 781.

4. Louis Ménard, *Rêveries d'un païen mystique*, éd. déf. (Paris, 1911), p. 211.

5. Sully Prudhomme, *Œuvres* (Paris: Alphonse Lemerre, 1886), III, Prologue, *La Justice*, p. 53.

6. Edouard Rod, *Les Idées morales du temps présent* (Paris, 1897), p. 82.

7. *A Survey of French Literature*, ed. Morris Bishop (New York, 1955), II, p. 215.

8. Olmsted, p. 111. Edmond About, *L'Homme à l'oreille cassée* (Paris, 1900).

9. Cf. Robert Ricatte, *La Création romanesque chez les Goncourt* (Paris, 1953), p. 41.

10. Gustave Flaubert, *Œuvres complètes, Correspondance*, Nouvelle éd. augmentée (Paris, 1930), VII, p. 384; VIII, p. 4.

11. Émile Zola, *Œuvres complètes, Thérèse Raquin*, V (Paris: Fasquelle, 1920), p. ix.

12. Zola, p. xiii.

13. Cf. Guy Robert, *Émile Zola* (Paris, 1952), p. 37; F. W. J. Hemmings, *Émile Zola* (Oxford, 1953), p. 121; J. H. Matthews, *Les Deux Zola* (Geneva, 1957), p. 10.

14. Auriant, *La Véritable Histoire de "Nana"* (Paris, 1942), p. 96.

15. Zola, *Œuvres complètes, Le Roman expérimental*, XIV, p. 46.

16. Robert, p. 37; Henri Martineau, *Le Roman scientifique d'Émile Zola* (Paris, 1907), pp. 33-43. The Anatole France quotation is from *L'Art Littéraire*, 2m série *Œuvres complètes illustrées* (Paris, 1922), VI, pp. 607-608.

17. Zola, *Le Roman expérimental*, pp. 69-74.

18. Goncourt, *Journal*, VIII, p. 202.

19. Goncourt, *Journal*, XVII, pp. 18-19.

20. Zola, *Le Roman expérimental*, p. 354. Notes.

21. Matthews, p. 53; Denise le Blond-Zola, *Émile Zola raconté par sa fille* (Paris, 1931), pp. 194-195.

22. Martineau, p. 69.

23. Zola, *Le docteur Pascal, Œuvres complètes*, XXXV, p. 197.

24. Zola, *Le docteur Pascal*, pp. 296-297. Cf. *Le Roman expérimental*, pp. 25, 30; Bernard, IEME, pp. 134, 143.

25. Goncourt insinuates that it was the nine-day wonder of Brown-Séquard: the injection of the male hormone thought to have restorative powers. *Journal*, XVIII, p. 215; XIX, p. 87.

26. Maurice Barrès, *Mes Cahiers* (Paris, 1933), VI, p. 147.

27. Paul Bourget, *Le Disciple,* Nelson ed. (Paris, n.d.), p. 191. "Ces savants vivisectaient des animaux. N'allais-je pas moi, vivisecter longuement une âme?" A similar reference to Bernard is found in his earlier novel *Mensonges* (Paris, 1890), p. 514.

28. Bourget, *Le Sens de la mort* (Paris, 1916), pp. 10 f., 138.

29. Bourget, *Nos Actes nous suivent* (Paris, 1927), I, pp. 14-17.

30. *Nos Actes nous suivent,* II, p. 243.

31. *Nos Actes nous suivent,* II, p. 33.

32. *Nos Actes nous suivent,* II, p. 34.

33. Bourget, *Sociologie et littérature,* 3rd series of *Études et portraits* (Paris, 1906), pp. 18-19, 42-43.

34. Bourget, *Pages de critique,* II, p. 143. Cf. also pp. 13-14, and *Au Service de l'ordre* (Paris, 1929), p. 26.

CHAPTER SEVEN

1. Georges Duhamel, *Mercure de France* (Aug. 1913), CIV, p. 599; Jules Romains, *Les Hommes de bonne Volonté,* XII, *Les Créateurs* (Paris, 1936), pp. 51, 72; André Gide, *Journal,* Pléiade ed. (Paris, 1948), I, pp. 981, 1331; (1954), II, p. 307. See René Leriche's discussion of Paul Valéry and Bernard. *La Chirurgie discipline de l'intelligence* (Paris, 1949), pp. 413-416. "Paul Valéry et l'esprit scientifique."

2. Antoine-Augustin Cournot, *An Essay on the Foundations of Our Knowledge,* trans. M. H. Moore (New York, 1956), p. 203, note.

3. Bergson, "La Philosophie de Claude Bernard," pp. 233-235.

4. *Phénomènes,* I, 51.

5. Georges Sorel, "Vues sur les Problèmes de la philosophie," *RMM,* (Jan. 1911), XIX, pp. 9-17.

6. Niels Bohr, *Atomic Physics and Human Knowledge* (New York, 1958), pp. 13-22; 94-101.

7. "Point de vue binaire," in Bernard's *Le Cahier rouge,* p. 66.

8. Edwin H. Ackerknecht, *Rudolf Virchow, Doctor Statesman Anthropologist* (Madison, 1953), p. 106; also Josiah Royce's introd. to translation of Poincaré, *Science and Hypothesis* (New York, 1913), p. 21.

9. *Principes,* p. 254.

10. Ackerknecht, p. 106.

11. Alfred Weber, *History of Philosophy,* trans. Thilly (New York, 1896), pp. 583 f.

12. Benrubi, I, p. 326 f., 332.

13. *Principes,* p. 121.

14. *Leçons de pathologie expérimentale,* p. 523. Cf. "Il n'y a pas de causes. Les phénomènes ne s'engendrent pas; ils se rencontrent." ("There are no causes. Phenomena do not engender each other; they meet.") *Pensées,* p. 81.

15. For such an approach, cf. Pierre Vendryès, *Vie et Probabilité* (Paris, 1942), p. 352. *Déterminisme et Autonomie* (Paris, 1956), *passim.* Vendryès, a great admirer of Bernard, began with an M. D. thesis on the subject *Les "Conditions Déterminées" de Claude Bernard* (Paris, 1940).

16. Flaubert, *Correspondance*, III, p. 333.

17. *Lettres beaujolaises*, p. 126. Cf. Lamy, *Claude Bernard et le matérialisme*, p. 85; Jacques Chevalier, "La Philosophie de Claude Bernard," in *Philosophie*, p. 55.

18. Père Didon, "Claude Bernard," *Revue de France* (1878), extrait, pp. 20-21. The Bibliothèque Nationale copy is inscribed by Didon himself.

19. Sertillanges, p. 38. Lamy, p. 25. They adopt the wording of the article as printed in the magazine *Revue de France*, Vol. 28, March 1, 1878, p. 21.

20. *Le Cahier rouge*, p. 97.

21. *Le Cahier rouge*, p. 141.

22. *Philosophie*, p. 23.

23. *Lettres beaujolaises*, p. xxvii. See also Sophie O'Brien, *Silhouettes d'Autrefois* (Paris, 1926), p. 13.

24. Georges Barral, who certainly seemed closer to Bernard than Didon, testified as follows: A month and a half before his death, walking with Barral and seeing a funeral go by, with a priest in a funeral coach, Bernard said to Barral: "When they take me to the graveyard, I hope I won't have such a companion!"

    "But," said Barral, "you have an ecclesiastic attending your course."

    "Yes, I do," he said. "He seems to be a good fellow; but his presence bothers me whenever I have to give a philosophical conclusion to my lecture, for I wouldn't like to cause him pain."

    Letter of Georges Barral printed in *Le Bien Public*, March 25, 1878.

25. Archives Claude Bernard, no. 49, cited by Chevalier, in *Philosophie*, p. 50.

26. Delhoume, *De Claude Bernard à D'Arsonval*, p. 32.

27. Lenoir, "Claude Bernard et l'Esprit expérimental," applies the term "rationalisme expérimental" to the philosophy of Bernard. P. 101.

28. Henry Adams, *The Education of Henry Adams, an Autobiography* (New York, 1918), p. 454.

29. *Principes*, pp. 172-173; IEME, p. 294.

INDEX

153